ELEMENTS OF ACOUSTICS

ENGLAND: BUTTERWORTH & CO. (PUBLISHERS) LTD.
                    LONDON: 88 KINGSWAY, W.C.2.

AUSTRALIA: BUTTERWORTH & CO. (AUSTRALIA) LTD.
                    SYDNEY: 6/8 O'CONNELL STREET
                    MELBOURNE: 473 BOURKE STREET
                    BRISBANE: 240 QUEEN STREET

CANADA: BUTTERWORTH & CO. (CANADA) LTD.
                    TORONTO: 1367 DANFORTH AVENUE, 6

NEW ZEALAND: BUTTERWORTH & CO. (NEW ZEALAND) LTD.
                    WELLINGTON: 49/51 BALLANCE STREET
                    AUCKLAND: 35 HIGH STREET

SOUTH AFRICA: BUTTERWORTH & CO. (SOUTH AFRICA) LTD.
                    DURBAN: 33/35 BEACH GROVE

U.S.A.:   BUTTERWORTH INC.
                    WASHINGTON, D.C.: 7235 WISCONSIN AVENUE, 14

ELEMENTS OF
ACOUSTICS

J. BLITZ, M.Sc., A.Inst.P.

Senior Lecturer in Physics
Brunel College
London

LONDON
BUTTERWORTHS
1964

Suggested U.D.C. No.: 534

Printed in Great Britain by The Lewes Press Wightman & Co. Ltd., Lewes, Sussex.

PREFACE

In recent years the subject of Acoustics has grown considerably in importance, and its range of applications, such as noise measurements, ultrasonic testing, the design of public address systems, etc., is now far reaching. It extends well beyond the realms of physicists and electrical engineers, and a thorough background knowledge of its fundamentals is useful, and often essential, to aeronautical, civil, mechanical, and production engineers, architects, builders, and even, in many instances, medical practitioners, biologists, and psychologists. In spite of all this, the subject is still often neglected in Physics courses at schools and colleges. The little that is taught is usually treated from an archaic point of view; far too many so-called modern text-books on Sound devote much attention to such historic curiosities as sonometers, phonic wheels, and Melde's experiment.

The object here is to present the subject in a concise, simplified, and up-to-date manner and to concentrate mainly on fundamental principles; the reader who requires information on experimental details and applications is directed to the references given at the end of each chapter. To keep the book reasonably short and thus inexpensive, it was decided to restrict it to an account of low amplitude elastic wave propagation at both audio- and ultrasonic frequencies. Those topics, such as shock waves and high energy ultrasonics, which have been left out are felt to require more specialist treatment and it is impossible to do proper justice to them in a book of this nature.

As far as possible Royal Society recommendations have been adopted for symbols, but there has been no hesitation in departing from them where they are considered to be unsuitable. Except in a few familiar cases the use of Greek symbols has been avoided.

This book was written to fulfil the needs of engineers, scientists, and others interested in the subject, and no particular examination syllabus has been followed. However, it

v

should be of value to those studying in the early years of Degree and Diploma in Technology courses and also to Higher National Certificate and Diploma students.

The author wishes to thank the various sources of information acknowledged in the text, Dr. G. F. Lewin for reading the manuscript and making some valuable suggestions, and Mr. G. E. Haines for assisting with the proof-reading. He does, however, accept full responsibility for any errors which may be found.

J. BLITZ

March 1964

CONTENTS

Preface   v

1   Elastic Vibrations   1

2   Propagation of Sound Waves   15

3   Reflection and Deviation of Sound Waves   30

4   The Velocity and Absorption of Sound Waves   49

5   Electromechanical and Electroacoustical Analogies   65

6   Hearing, Loudness, and Noise   80

7   Acoustics of Buildings   89

8   The Generation, Reception, and Recording of Sound   99

9   Fundamental Acoustic Measurements   119

Index   135

ELASTIC VIBRATIONS

Introduction

Sound waves are produced as a result of a mechanical disturbance taking place in a material medium. The energy from this disturbance is transmitted through the medium and may be picked up by a suitably placed receiver. One can classify these waves into two categories, one in which the material is strained within the elastic limit (i.e., Hooke's law holds) and the other in which the material is strained beyond the elastic limit. The first type of waves is called elastic waves; these are responsible for most of the observed acoustic phenomena and this book is almost entirely devoted to the discussion of their properties. The second category of waves covers such phenomena as shock waves and high energy ultrasonic propagation. These are independent subjects and an adequate treatment of them is impossible in a book of this nature; the interested reader is recommended to consult the works of Courant and Friedrichs[1] and Crawford[2], respectively.

Simple Harmonic Motion

The production, propagation, and detection of sound waves are usually related to the setting up of periodic oscillations. The simplest of these is called simple harmonic motion, and when a body vibrates with such motion a pure tone having a single frequency is emitted.

A particle is said to execute simple harmonic motion when its motion along a line is such that its displacement from a given point on that line varies in direct proportion with its acceleration towards that point. Thus if y represents the value of the displacement and $-d^2y/dt^2$ the value of the acceleration, the negative sign indicating that the acceleration decreases with increase in displacement, we have:

$$d^2y/dt^2 + \omega^2 y = 0 \qquad \dots (1.1)$$

where ω is a constant. The solution to this equation can be shown to be (see, for example, Sokolnikoff[3], page 233):

$$y = y_0 \cos (\omega t + \theta) \qquad \ldots (1.2)$$

where y_0 is the magnitude of the maximum value, i.e. the amplitude of y, and is equal to y_0 when $(\omega t + \theta)$ is equal to zero, i.e. the variation is sinusoidal. *Figure 1* illustrates the

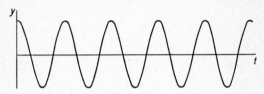

Figure 1. Variation of displacement y with time t for simple harmonic motion

variation of y with time t; this follows a sinusoidal curve. It is seen that a complete vibration occurs in the time period T given by the equation:

$$T = 2\pi / \omega \qquad \ldots (1.3)$$

The frequency f of the oscillations is defined as the number of complete vibrations occurring in unit time, i.e. $F = 1/T$; $\omega = 2\pi f$ is called the angular frequency or pulsatance; $(\omega t + \theta)$ is called the phase angle—this is equal to θ when t is equal to zero.

If we put $y = y_0$ when $t = 0$, the value of θ becomes zero and we have:

$$y = y_0 \cos \omega t \qquad \ldots (1.4a)$$

On the other hand, if $y = 0$ when $t = 0$, θ becomes equal to $\pi / 2$ and we have that:

$$y = y_0 \sin \omega t \qquad \ldots (1.4b)$$

These alternative expressions may be obtained by taking the real and imaginary parts, respectively, of the expression:

$$y = y_0 \exp j\omega t \qquad \ldots (1.5)$$

where $j = (-1)^{\frac{1}{2}}$.

2

Lissajous Figures

Consider a particle being subjected simultaneously to two simple harmonic motions in directions at right-angles to one another and let their respective displacements be represented by the equations:

$$y' = y_1 \cos \omega_1 t$$

and

$$y'' = y_2 \cos (\omega_2 t + \theta)$$

At any time t the resultant position of the particle is given by the co-ordinates y' and y''.

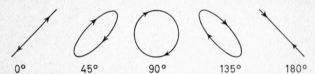

| 0° | 45° | 90° | 135° | 180° |

Figure 2. Lissajous figures from two simple harmonic motions at right-angles having the same frequency but varying in phase differences

Figure 2 shows the positions of the particle for all values of t for different values of θ when $\omega_1 = \omega_2$. When θ is equal to zero and integral values of π, i.e. π, 2π, etc., the cyclic motion of the particle is along a straight line. For all other values of θ the traces are ellipses. In the special case where y_1 is equal to y_2 and the value of θ is an odd integral of $\pi/2$, e.g. 90 degrees and 270 degrees, the trace of the particle is a circle. A cyclic pattern traced out by a particle in this way is called a Lissajous figure.

When the two frequencies are not equal the patterns are more complex; the time taken for a single cycle of the pattern to be described is the period elapsing between two consecutive occasions when the vibrations are in phase with one another, i.e., their phase angles are the same or differ by multiples of 2π. Where the ratio of the frequencies is a simple one, the patterns are simple (see *Figure 3*). A more complete account of Lissajous figures has been given by Sharman[4].

A convenient method of studying Lissajous figures is to apply two sinusoidal voltages of the required frequencies to

3

the X and Y plates, respectively, of a cathode ray oscilloscope and to observe the trace on the screen.

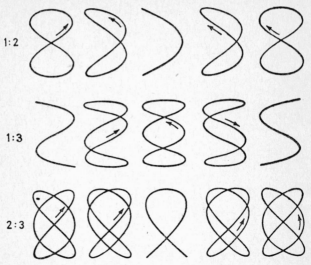

Figure 3. *Lissajous figures from two simple harmonic motions at right-angles having different frequency ratios and varying in phase differences*

(From Sharman[4].)

Beats

Beats are produced when two simple harmonic motions of slightly different frequencies having amplitudes of the same order of magnitude act along the same line. Let these motions be represented by the expressions:

$$y' = y_1 \cos \omega t \quad \text{and} \quad y'' = y_2 \cos (\omega + \Delta\omega) t$$

where $\Delta\omega$ is small. In any given time t the resultant displacement y is given by:

$$y = y_1 \cos \omega t + y_2 \cos (\omega + \Delta\omega) t$$

or

$$y = 2y_2 \cos (\Delta\omega / 2) t \cos (\omega + \Delta\omega / 2) t + (y_1 - y_2) \cos \omega t$$

$$\dots . (1.6)$$

The first term on the right-hand side of equation 1.6 has an amplitude which varies with time, i.e. modulation occurs, and *Figure 4* shows the variation for $y_1 = y_2$. Where the vibrations

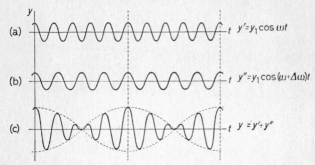

Figure 4. Formation of beats caused by the addition of two simple harmonic motions of equal amplitudes and of nearly equal frequencies

give rise to audible sound waves the ear cannot distinguish between positive and negative values of y but only between maximum and minimum values of intensity (see under Control of Vibrations, page 13). Since the intensity is proportional to the square of the amplitude, maximum intensity will be observed when the first term on the right-hand side of equation 1.6 is equal to $\pm 2y_2$, for which $\cos(\Delta\omega/2)\,t = \pm 1$ and minimum intensity when this term is equal to zero, i.e. $\cos(\Delta\omega/2)\,t = 0$. Maxima will thus be observed twice per cycle with a time period equal to $2\pi/\Delta\omega$. Thus the amplitude modulation frequency, or the beat frequency, is equal to the difference $\Delta\omega/2\pi$ between the two emitted frequencies.

Complex Periodic Vibrations

It is rare for a sound to be emitted at a single frequency from a source. In Chapter 3, page 40, it is shown that a vibrating body can emit a note at a fundamental frequency together with a number or overtones known as harmonics or partials whose frequencies have values which are multiples of the fundamental, e.g., the frequency of the nth harmonic is equal to n times the fundamental frequency. The number and relative amplitudes of the various harmonics present depend on the characteristics of the source and will determine the quality, or timbre, of the note.

Fourier has shown that any periodic motion consists of the sum of a number of simple harmonic motions, each having a frequency which is a harmonic of the fundamental. Thus:

$$y = a_0 + a_1 \cos \omega t + a_2 \cos 2\omega t + a_3 \cos 3\omega t + \ldots a_n \cos n\omega t$$
$$+ b_1 \sin \omega t + b_2 \sin 2\omega t + b_3 \sin 3\omega t + \ldots b_n \sin n\omega t$$
$$= \sum_{n=0}^{n=\infty} a_n \cos n\omega t + \sum_{n=0}^{n=\infty} b_n \sin n\omega t \qquad \ldots \ldots (1.7)$$

where a_0, a_1, $a_2 \ldots b_1$, $b_2 \ldots$ are constants. Thus waveforms such as those shown in *Figure 5* can be broken down in this way. *Figure 5a* shows a rectangular waveform as consisting of the sum of simple harmonic motions having the fundamental frequency and odd harmonics of that frequency. *Figure 5b* shows a triangular waveform consisting also of the fundamental frequency and the odd harmonics of that frequency, except that there is a phase difference of 180 degrees between consecutive components. This method of resolution is called Fourier analysis (see, for example, Sokolnikoff[3], page 63).

Free Damped Vibrations

Elastic waves may be propagated as a result of either a periodic or aperiodic (i.e., non-periodic) motion caused by a disturbance. This can be conveniently represented by the motion of a mass M at one end of a helical spring, having its other end clamped in position. The compliance C_m (i.e., the displacement per unit restoring force) of the spring remains constant at all times if elastic conditions are to apply (i.e., Hooke's law is obeyed). Let the mass be displaced along the direction of the axis of the spring by some amount y_0 and then released. At any time t the total energy E_m of the system is given by the sum of the kinetic energy $\frac{1}{2}M (dy/dt)^2$ of the mass and the elastic energy $\frac{1}{2}y^2/C_m$ stored in the

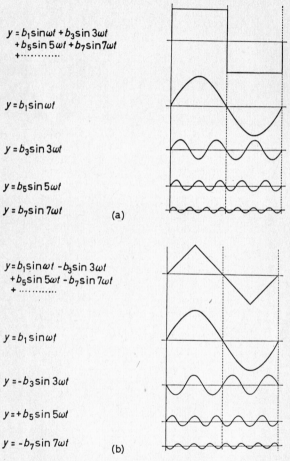

$y = b_1 \sin \omega t + b_3 \sin 3\omega t$
$\quad + b_5 \sin 5\omega t + b_7 \sin 7\omega t$
$\quad + \cdots\cdots$

$y = b_1 \sin \omega t$

$y = b_3 \sin 3\omega t$

$y = b_5 \sin 5\omega t$

$y = b_7 \sin 7\omega t \qquad \text{(a)}$

$y = b_1 \sin \omega t - b_3 \sin 3\omega t$
$\quad + b_5 \sin 5\omega t - b_7 \sin 7\omega t$
$\quad + \cdots\cdots$

$y = b_1 \sin \omega t$

$y = -b_3 \sin 3\omega t$

$y = +b_5 \sin 5\omega t$

$y = -b_7 \sin 7\omega t \qquad \text{(b)}$

Figure 5. Analyses of waveforms into simple harmonic components by Fourier's method, showing in each case the first four components

7

spring (i.e., potential energy) where y represents the displacement of the mass from its mean position, i.e.

$$E_m = \tfrac{1}{2} M \, (dy/dt)^2 + \tfrac{1}{2} y^2 / C_m \qquad \ldots (1.8)$$

Let us assume that this energy is dissipated only in overcoming frictional forces and that, for small values of velocity, this force varies directly in proportion to velocity and is equal to $R_m \, (dy/dt)$, where R_m is the frictional force per unit velocity, or mechanical resistance. The rate of dissipation of energy is thus given by the expression:

$$- dE_m/dt = R_m \, (dy/dt)^2 \qquad \ldots (1.9)$$

If it is assumed that, since the system is a moving one, the solution $dy/dt = 0$ is invalid for all values of y, equations 1.8 and 1.9 yield:

$$M d^2 y/dt^2 + R_m dy/dt + y/C_m = 0 \qquad \ldots (1.10)$$

Equation 1.10 is a differential equation of the second order, similar in form to the equation representing the discharge of an electrical capacitance C through an inductance L in series with a resistance R. Thus M, R_m, C_m, and y are respectively analogous to L, R, C and the charge q. If it is assumed that the solution is exponential in form, we obtain:

$$y = \exp\left(-R_m/2M\right) t \left\{ A \exp \left(R_m^2 / 4M^2 - 1/C_m M\right)^{\frac{1}{2}} t \right.$$
$$\left. + B \exp -\left(R_m^2 / 4M^2 - 1/C_m M\right)^{\frac{1}{2}} t \right\} \ldots (1.11)$$

where A and B are constants, the values of which are determined by the application of the proper boundary conditions. The final form of equation 1.11 is determined from one of the four following conditions:

(a) $R_m^2 / 4M^2$ is greater than $1/C_m M$, i.e., the motion of the mass is heavily damped. The solution remains in the form of equation 1.11 which represents a negative exponential decrease in the value of y with time; the motion is said to be aperiodic.

(b) $R_m^2 / 4M^2$ is equal to $1/C_m M$. The solution as expressed by equation 1.11 is indeterminate and thus does not hold

FREE DAMPED VIBRATIONS

If it is assumed that a solution of equation 1.10 is given by:

$$y = \tau \exp\left(-R_m/2M\right)t$$

where τ is a function of t, we finally obtain the result:

$$y = (A + Bt)\exp\left(-R_m/2M\right)t \qquad \ldots (1.12)$$

where A and B are both constants. The expression $A + Bt$ increases with time at a much slower rate than the exponential term decreases with time. This is the case of critical damping, for which the system comes to rest in the minimum time.

(c) R_m is equal to zero. Equation 1.10 then reduces to an equation representing simple harmonic motion. The solution to this is

$$y = A \exp j \left(1/C_mM\right)^{\frac{1}{2}} t + B \exp -j \left(1/C_mM\right)^{\frac{1}{2}} t \quad \ldots (1.13)$$

where $j = (-1)^{\frac{1}{2}}$. Applying the boundary conditions $y = y_0$ and $dy/dt = 0$ when $t = 0$, the solution reduces to:

$$y = y_0 \cos \omega_0 t \qquad \ldots (1.13a)$$

where $\omega_0 = (1/C_mM)^{\frac{1}{2}}$; i.e., the motion is sinusoidal with the time period T given by the equation:

$$T = 2\pi/\omega_0 = 2\pi \left(C_mM\right)^{\frac{1}{2}} \qquad \ldots (1.14)$$

(d) $R_m^2/4M^2$ is less than $1/C_mM$. The solution to equation 1.10 may then be written in the form:

$$y = \exp -\alpha't \left(A \exp j\omega t + B \exp -j\omega t\right)$$

or

$$y = \exp -\alpha't . C \cos \left(\omega t - \phi\right) \qquad \ldots (1.15)$$

where $C = (A^2 + B^2)^{\frac{1}{2}}$ and $\phi = \tan^{-1}(A/B)$. Here $\alpha' = (R_m/2M)$ and $\omega^2 = 1/C_mM - R_m^2/4M^2 = \omega_0^2 - \alpha'^2$.

Applying the boundary conditions $y = y_0$ and $dy/dt = 0$ when $t = 0$, we have:

$$\alpha' = \sin \phi \quad \text{and} \quad C = y_0/\cos \phi = y_0/(1 - \alpha'^2)^{\frac{1}{2}}$$

and equation 1.15 becomes:

B

9

ELASTIC VIBRATIONS

$$y = \exp\left(-\alpha' t\right)\{C/(1-\alpha'^2)^{\frac{1}{2}}\}\cos\left(\omega t - \phi\right) \quad \ldots (1.15a)$$

The time period T is then given by the expression

$$T = 2\pi/\omega = 2\pi/(1/C_m M - R_m^2/4M^2)^{\frac{1}{2}}$$
$$= 2\pi/(\omega_0^2 - \alpha'^2)^{\frac{1}{2}} = 2\pi/\omega_0 (1 - \alpha'^2/\omega_0^2)^{\frac{1}{2}} \quad \ldots (1.16)$$

For sufficiently small damping, i.e., when the oscillations are sustained at an observable level for at least three or four periods, the term α'/ω_0 becomes small enough for $\omega \simeq \omega_0$ and for equation 1.15a to reduce to the approximation

$$y = \exp\left(-\alpha' t\right) y_0 \cos \omega_0 t \qquad \ldots (1.17)$$

The variation of y with t for damped harmonic motion is illustrated in *Figure 6*. The approximation which yields equation 1.17 gives rise to the assumption that the peaks and troughs of the curve lie on negative exponential envelopes.

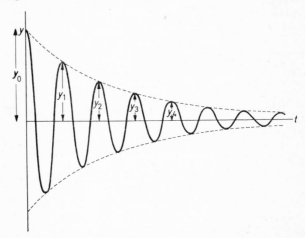

Figure 6. Damped harmonic oscillations

The amplitudes of consecutive peaks in *Figure 6* have respective values y_0, y_1, $y_2 \ldots y_n$ at the times 0, T, $2T \ldots nT$, where n is an integer. The logarithmic decrement δ is defined by the expression:

$$\exp \delta = y_0/y_1 = y_1/y_2 = y_2/y_3 = \ldots = y_{n-1}/y_n \quad \ldots (1.18)$$

so that

$$\delta = \alpha' T = R_m T/2M \quad \ldots (1.19)$$

When y reaches a maximum value y_n, differentiation of equation 1.17 shows that the velocity dy/dt is zero and hence the kinetic energy of the mass must be zero. Equation 1.8 shows that the energy is entirely potential and thus equal to $\frac{1}{2}y_n^2/C_m$. The fractional loss of energy E_m per cycle is then given by the expression:

$$\Delta E_m/E_m = (E_{n-1} - E_n)/E_{n-1} = 1 - y_n^2/y_{n-1}^2$$
$$= 1 - \exp(-2\delta) \approx 2\delta \quad \ldots (1.20)$$

Forced Vibrations

When a periodic force $F = F_0 \sin \omega t$ having a frequency $f = \omega/2\pi$ is applied to the mass, the latter experiences forced oscillations of that frequency and the equation of motion becomes:

$$M (d^2y/dt^2) + R_m (dy/dt) + y/C_m = F_0 \sin \omega t$$
$$\ldots (1.21)$$

For steady conditions it can be shown by taking the particular integral (see, for example, Sokolnikoff[3], page 308) that the velocity $u = dy/dt$ at a given time t will be:

$$u = F/\{R_m + j(\omega M - 1/\omega C_m)\} \quad \ldots (1.22)$$

where $j = (-1)^{\frac{1}{2}}$, and the velocity amplitude u_0 is given by:

$$u_0 = F_0/\{R_m^2 + (\omega M - 1/\omega C_m)^2\}^{\frac{1}{2}} \quad \ldots (1.23)$$

Equations 1.21, 1.22, and 1.23 are identical in form with those which represent an electrical circuit containing a resistance R, an inductance L and a capacitance C in series with an alternating e.m.f. V. Thus R_m, M, C_m, and F are analogous to R, L, C, and V, respectively. y and u are respectively analogous to the electric charge q and current i. The ratio

$Z_m = F/u$ is consequently termed the mechanical impedance. This quantity, as seen from equation 1.22, is complex and thus may be written in the form

$$Z_m = R_m + jX_m \qquad \dots (1.24)$$

where $X_m = (\omega M - 1/\omega C_m)$ is called the mechanical reactance.

Resonance

Relationships between velocity amplitude and frequency, as given by equation 1.23, are shown in *Figure 7* for different values of R_m. These are called frequency response curves

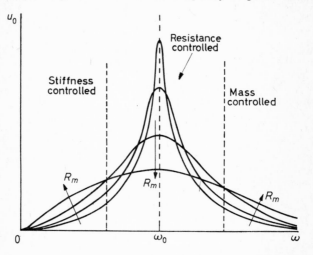

Figure 7. Variation of velocity amplitude u_0 with frequency for forced vibrations, where the applied periodic force has a constant amplitude for all frequencies

and are similar in form to those for electrical *LRC* circuits. The velocity amplitude for a given force is a maximum at a frequency $\omega_0/2\pi = (1/2\pi)(1/C_m M)^{\frac{1}{2}}$, where the reactive component of impedance is zero; resonance is then said to occur. This frequency is called the resonant frequency. The

12

quality of resonance is described by the mechanical 'Q' factor Q_m, which is defined by the relationship:

$$Q_m = \omega_0 M / R_m = \pi / \delta \qquad \dots (1.25)$$

The lower the value of R_m the higher the value of Q_m and, hence, the sharper the peaks of the curves. It will be left as an exercise to the reader to show that, approximately,

$$Q_m = \omega_0 / (\omega_2 - \omega_1) \qquad \dots (1.26)$$

where ω_1 and ω_2 represent, respectively, the angular frequencies on each side of ω_0 where the values of u_0 are both equal to the fraction $1/\sqrt{2}$ of the maximum value, occurring at ω_0.

Control of Vibrations

The amplitude of vibrations at a given frequency, as indicated by equation 1.23 and illustrated by *Figure 7*, depends on the impedance. The component of the impedance which is predominant in controlling the amplitude of the vibrations is a function of frequency. At low frequencies where $\omega \ll \omega_0$ the component ωM is generally small in comparison with $1/\omega C_m$ and it is the stiffness which is predominant, the stiffness being equal to the reciprocal $1/C_m$ of the compliance. The vibrations are then said to be stiffness controlled. At high frequencies where $\omega \gg \omega_0$, ωM is usually large compared with the term $1/\omega C_m$ and the vibrations are then said to be mass controlled or inertia controlled. At frequencies in the region of the resonant frequency the terms ωM and $1/\omega C_m$ tend to cancel one another out and it is the mechanical resistance R_m which becomes dominant; the vibrations are then said to be resistance controlled.

REFERENCES

[1] Courant, R. and Friedrichs, K. O. *Supersonic Flow and Shock Waves.* 1948. New York; Interscience

[2] Crawford, A. E. *Ultrasonic Engineering.* 1955. London; Butterworths

[3] Sokolnikoff, I. S. and Sokolnikoff, E. S. *Higher Mathematics for Engineers and Physicists,* 2nd ed. 1941. New York; McGraw-Hill

[4] Sharman, R. V. *Vibrations and Waves,* p. 41. 1963. London; Butterworths

FURTHER READING

Church, A. H. *Mechanical Vibrations.* 1957. New York; Wiley/London; Chapman and Hall

Morse, P. M. *Vibration and Sound,* 2nd ed. 1948. New York; McGraw-Hill

PROPAGATION OF SOUND WAVES

Wave Motion

The method of propagation of sound waves is probably best understood by referring to *Figure 8* which depicts a vibrating source and a receiver parallel with it. The medium between them, which is homogeneous, may be assumed to consist of a number of thin parallel layers. The source vibrates at a given frequency about its mean position and the energy of the vibrations is passed on to the adjoining layer *A* which will oscillate at the same frequency. Energy from *A* then passes to *B* and progressively to *C, D, E,* etc., which in turn will likewise oscillate. Eventually this energy arrives at the receiver which will then vibrate at the frequency of the source. Because a finite time period is required for the transmission of sound energy, the vibrations of each layer will lag in phase behind those of its predecessor. The leading surface of the waves is called the wavefront.

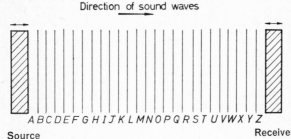

Direction of sound waves

A B C D E F G H I J K L M N O P Q R S T U V W X Y Z

Source   Receiver

Figure 8. Sound propagated in a medium divided into thin parallel layers

It must be made quite clear that the particles of the medium are not themselves travelling with the waves; they only vibrate about their mean positions. It is the energy which is moving away from the source.

Where the vibrations take place in the direction of the wave motion, longitudinal waves are said to be propagated. Since the layers in the medium are alternately compressed and expanded the longitudinal waves are also called compression waves. Where the vibrations occur in a direction at right-angles to that of the wave motion, transverse waves are propagated—these are also called shear waves if the layers of the medium suffer periodic shear stresses and strains. Liquids and gases cannot, as a rule, withstand shear stresses; hence shear waves can usually be propagated in solids only. In Chapter 4 an account is given of different kinds of transverse waves which are not shear waves.

For a source of sound waves in the form of a pulsating sphere, the vibrations are directed radially and sound waves are propagated uniformly in all directions, with the result that the wavefronts are spherical. Where the source of sound waves is a plane surface vibrating in such a way that all points on the surface are in phase, the wavefronts are plane. In the first case we have spherical waves and in the second case plane waves. In regions sufficiently far removed from a spherical source, the curvature of the wavefronts is so small that one can effectively regard the waves as being plane (see under Spherical Waves, page 23).

Equations of Motion of Plane Waves

Consider a plane source vibrating with simple harmonic motion described by the equation:

$$y = y_0 \cos \omega t \quad \text{(cf. equation 1.14)} \qquad \ldots (2.1)$$

at a frequency $f = \omega/2\pi$. If plane waves are travelling from the source in the x direction with a constant speed c they will arrive at some point A at a distance x from the source in a time $t' = x/c$. The phase of the vibrations at A will thus lag behind that of the source by an amount $\omega t'$ and the particle displacement y in the medium at A will be given by the expression:

$$y = y_0 \cos \omega (t - t')$$

i.e.

$$y = y_0 \cos \omega (t - x/c) \qquad \ldots (2.2a)$$

16

In a single time period T there will be a change in the phase angle of an amount 2π during which the waves will have travelled a distance $\lambda = cT$, where λ is called the wavelength. Thus we may write:

$$y = y_0 \cos 2\pi \, (t/T - x/\lambda) \qquad \ldots (2.2b)$$

or

$$y = y_0 \cos (\omega t - kx) \qquad \ldots (2.2c)$$

where $k = \omega/c = 2\pi/\lambda$ is called the wave number. Using the exponential form introduced in equation 1.5, this may be written as:

$$y = y_0 \exp j \, (\omega t - kx) \qquad \ldots (2.2d)$$

The particle velocity u may be written as:

$$u = \partial y/\partial t = -\omega y_0 \sin (\omega t - kx)$$

$$= \omega y_0 \sin (\omega t - kx + \pi) \qquad \ldots (2.3a)$$

or

$$u = j\omega y_0 \exp j \, (\omega t - kx)$$

$$= \omega y_0 \exp j \, (\omega t - kx + \pi/2) \qquad \ldots (2.3b)$$

Putting $u_0 = \omega y_0$, and choosing our time scale so that the phase angle is suitably retarded, we may express these relationships more conveniently as:

$$u = u_0 \sin (\omega t - kx) \qquad \ldots (2.3c)$$

or

$$u = u_0 \exp j \, (\omega t - kx) \qquad \ldots (2.3d)$$

where u_0 represents the velocity amplitude. It is seen that y and u differ in phase by 90 degrees.

If equation 2.2c is differentiated twice with respect to x and t, respectively, we have:

$$\partial^2 y/\partial x^2 = -k^2 y_0 \cos (\omega t - kx)$$

$$\partial^2 y/\partial t^2 = -\omega^2 y_0 \cos (\omega t - kx)$$

thus giving:

$$\partial^2 y/\partial t^2 = c^2 \partial^2 y/\partial x^2 \qquad \ldots (2.4a)$$

since $c = \omega/k$.

This is the general wave equation for plane waves. A similar expression may be obtained for the particle velocity u and another for the acoustic pressure p, i.e.

$$\partial^2 u / \partial t^2 = c^2 \partial^2 u / \partial x^2 \qquad \ldots. (2.4b)$$

and

$$\partial^2 p / \partial t^2 = c^2 \partial^2 p / \partial x^2 \qquad \ldots. (2.4c)$$

The Velocity of Plane Waves

Consider plane longitudinal waves propagated in the x direction in a homogeneous medium of uniform density ρ. Let AB (see *Figure 9*) represent a thin parallel-sided layer of

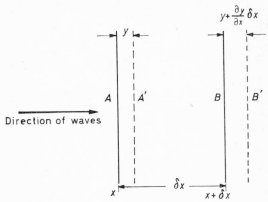

Figure 9. Strain of a layer of homogeneous material due to the passage of longitudinal plane waves through it

the medium, with its surfaces A and B normal to the direction of propagation and at respective distances x and $x + \delta x$ from some origin. Now at some time t the wave motion causes A to be displaced to a position A' by an amount y, so that its distance from the origin along the x direction is increased to an amount $x + y$; B is then displaced to a position B'. This latter displacement, which is assumed to be small, will be, to a first order of approximation, equal to $y + (\partial y / \partial x)\,\delta x$.

For a cross-section of unit area, the mechanical strain

18

suffered by the layer AB is seen to be equal to $\partial y/\partial x$. If p represents the acoustic pressure, i.e. the excess pressure caused by the passage of the sound waves, which gives rise to this strain, we have in accordance with Hooke's law that:

$$p = -q\partial y/\partial x \qquad \ldots (2.5)$$

where q is the appropriate modulus of elasticity of the medium for the type of stress exerted. In this case the layer is compressed and a positive stress will thus produce a negative strain. For sound propagation the variations in strain occur so rapidly that there is no time for the system to settle down to a state of equilibrium. Because, in addition, little or no time is available for heat exchanges between adjoining layers of the medium, adiabatic conditions are assumed to hold and the adiabatic value of the elastic modulus must be used. This is greater than the isothermal (i.e., static) value by a factor γ, the ratio of the specific heat at constant pressure to the specific heat at constant volume (see, for example, Newman and Searle[1]). For solids and liquids the value of this ratio is so close to unity that the two values can be taken as being equal for most practical purposes.

Consider another layer CD, similar to AB, in the medium and let the values of the acoustic pressures at C and D be p and $p + (\partial p/\partial x)\,\delta x$, respectively. In accordance with Newton's third law of motion, equal and opposite pressures act on each of the boundaries C and D. This layer is thus compressed by an amount $+p$ at C and $-\{p + (\partial p/\partial x)\,\delta x\}$ at D, with the result that there is an unbalanced pressure equal to $-(\partial p/\partial x)\,\delta x$ acting on the layer. This imparts an acceleration, in accordance with Newton's second law, and the pressure can be expressed as $\rho\delta x\partial^2 y/\partial t^2$. Hence:

$$\partial p/\partial x = -\rho\partial^2 y/\partial t^2 \qquad \ldots (2.6)$$

Equations 2.5 and 2.6 thus give:

$$\partial^2 y/\partial t^2 = (q/\rho)\,\partial^2 y/\partial x^2 \qquad \ldots (2.7)$$

and, from equations 2.4 and 2.7, we obtain:

$$c = (q/\rho)^{\frac{1}{2}} \qquad \ldots (2.8)$$

A similar result can be obtained for shear waves.

In Chapter 4, equation 2.8 will be applied to different types of waves in various kinds of media.

Specific Acoustic Impedance

In Chapter 1, page 12, the term mechanical impedance is defined as a result of the analogy of mechanical with electrical vibrations. A similar type of analogy exists between acoustical and electrical vibrations, in which the acoustic pressure p, the particle displacement y, and the particle velocity u are equivalent to potential difference, electric charge, and electric current, respectively. One can thus define the specific acoustic impedance Z_a as the ratio of acoustic pressure to particle velocity, i.e.:

$$Z_a = p/u \qquad \qquad \dots (2.9)$$

This is analogous to electrical impedance and is equal to the mechanical impedance per unit area of cross-section of the medium. Like both electrical and mechanical impedance, Z_a is complex and can be expressed as:

$$Z_a = R_a + jX_a \qquad \qquad \dots (2.10)$$

where R_a and X_a are the respective resistive and reactive components.

For plane progressive waves in a non-absorbent medium, we have:

$$p = -q\partial y/\partial x = -qky_0 \sin(\omega t - kx)$$

in accordance with equations 2.5 and 2.2c. Using the value of u given by equation 2.3a, one obtains:

$$Z_a = p/u = qk/\omega = q/c = \rho c \qquad \qquad \dots (2.11)$$

since from equation 2.8, $q = \rho c^2$.

Here Z_a is real and, because there is no reactive component, it must be equal to R_a. The product ρc is called the characteristic impedance for the medium. For spherical waves (see under Spherical Waves, p. 25), and plane stationary waves (see Chapter 5, p. 75), Z_a is complex.

20

Acoustic Intensity

Consider some point in a sound field and imagine a very small plane surface, normal to the direction of propagation and having an area δA, containing that point. If δW is the rate of flow of energy through that surface, the ratio $\delta W / \delta A$ is defined as the average acoustic intensity over the area. Proceeding to the limit, $\delta A \longrightarrow 0$, i.e., the area of the point in question, we have

$$I = dW / dA \qquad \qquad \dots (2.12)$$

where I represents the acoustic intensity at that point.

Let spherical waves be propagated from a point source in a uniform, isotropic, non-absorbent medium and let W be the value of the power of the source. The intensity at any point at a distance r from the source is obtained by dividing the rate of flow of energy, which will be uniform in all directions and equal to the power of the source, by the total surface area of a sphere of radius r with the source as centre, i.e.,

$$I = W / 4\pi r^2 \qquad \qquad \dots (2.13)$$

The intensity thus falls off with distance from the source in accordance with the inverse square law.

For plane waves propagated in a uniform non-absorbent medium, the principle of conservation of energy shows that the value of I must be the same for all points in the sound field. Let E represent the energy density of the sound waves, i.e., the energy per unit volume of the sound field. Because the energy passes through a unit cross-section with a velocity c, the length and, hence, the volume of the column of energy flowing in unit time must be numerically equal to c. The total energy in this column is then equal to cE. Thus:

$$I = cE \qquad \qquad \dots (2.14)$$

The energy E_m of the vibrations of a single particle of mass M in the medium, as given by equation 1.8, may be expressed as:

$$E_m = \tfrac{1}{2}Mu^2 + \tfrac{1}{2}y^2 / C_m$$

Where the output of the source is constant the value of E_m must be constant for all values of time t. If we choose a value of t corresponding to $y = 0$, equations 2.2 and 2.3 show that $u = u_0$; hence we have that $E_m = \frac{1}{2}Mu_0^2$ For unit volume of the medium, the value of M is numerically the same as the density ρ, and E_m is numerically equal to the energy density. Thus:

$$E = \tfrac{1}{2}\rho u_0^2 \qquad \text{.... (2.15)}$$

Hence:

$$I = cE = \tfrac{1}{2}\rho c u_0^2 = \tfrac{1}{2}R_a u_0^2 \qquad \text{.... (2.16)}$$

where $R_a = \rho c$, see equation 2.11. This equation is analogous to the relationship between the electrical power W_e, the peak current i_0, and the resistance R, i.e.,

$$W_e = \tfrac{1}{2}i_0^2 R$$

Equation 2.16 may be expressed alternatively as

$$I = \tfrac{1}{2}p_0^2/\rho c \quad (\text{cf. } W_e = \tfrac{1}{2}V_0^2/R) \qquad \text{.... (2.17)}$$

where V_0 represents the peak voltage, or

$$I = \tfrac{1}{2}p_0 u_0 \quad (\text{cf. } W_e = \tfrac{1}{2}V_0 i_0) \qquad \text{.... (2.18)}$$

or

$$I = \tfrac{1}{2}\rho c \omega^2 y_0^2 \qquad \text{.... (2.19)}$$

These equations show that the intensity I varies in proportion with the square of the amplitude A, as represented by either y_0, u_0, or p_0. Variations of intensity or amplitude are often expressed in terms of the decibel (dB), as follows:

Increase in sound level $= 10 \log_{10} (I/I_0) = 20 \log_{10} (A/A_0)$ dB
$$\text{.... (2.20)}$$

where the subscript zero indicates the initial value.

Pressure of Radiation

Because sound waves consist of energy in motion, it is to be expected that a steady pressure will be exerted on an obstacle placed in an acoustic field. Now the intensity, as shown in equation 2.12, is equal to the power per unit area, and since power may be expressed as the product of force and velocity, intensity will be equal to the product of a pressure P_r and the wave velocity c, i.e.,

$$I = P_r c \qquad \ldots (2.21)$$

P_r is the steady pressure exerted by the sound waves and it is called the pressure of radiation. A comparison of equation 2.21 with equation 2.14 shows that this is equal to the energy density E.

Attenuation of Plane Waves

It has been assumed up to now that the intensity is the same in all parts of a beam of plane waves, irrespective of the distance from the source. This may not be true for one or more of the following reasons: (a) deviation of energy from the parallel beam due to diffraction; (b) scattering, and (c) absorption, where the sound energy is converted into heat by internal friction in the medium.

For plane waves the relationship between loss of energy and distance is often expressed by the absorption coefficient α as follows:

$$A = A_0 \exp - \alpha x \qquad \ldots (2.22a)$$

i.e.,

$$I = I_0 \exp - 2\alpha x \qquad \ldots (2.22b)$$

This is sometimes expressed in népers per cm but it is now becoming common practice to measure attenuation on the decibel scale, 1 néper being equivalent to $8 \cdot 686$ dB.

Another way of expressing attenuation is by means of the loss per cycle (see Chapter 1, page 10) using the logarithmic decrement $\delta = \alpha \lambda$ or the 'Q' factor. Thus from equations 1.19 and 1.25 we have

$$\delta = \alpha \lambda = \alpha' T = \pi / Q_m \qquad \ldots (2.23)$$

Some of the more common factors giving rise to absorption are discussed in Chapter 4, page 61.

Spherical Waves

Consider a small sphere pulsating in a uniform isotropic medium. In doing so the surface expands and contracts radially about its mean position. Spherical waves are propagated uniformly in all directions as though originating from a point source. It has already been shown (see equation 2.13) that the intensity I decreases in a non-absorbent medium in accordance with the inverse square law. Equations 2.17 to 2.19 show that the intensity is proportional to the square of the amplitude; thus the pressure amplitude decreases, in inverse proportion, with distance r from the source. From equations 2.3d and 2.9 the acoustic pressure in plane waves is expressed by:

$$p = p_0 \exp j\,(\omega t - kx)$$

Modifying this equation to apply to spherical waves we have:

$$p = (A/r)\exp j\,(\omega t - kr) \qquad \ldots\,(2.24)$$

where A is a constant. Writing equation 2.24 in the form:

$$rp = A.\exp j\,(\omega t - kr)$$

and proceeding in the same manner as for plane waves (see page 16), we have:

$$\partial^2\,(rp)/\partial t^2 = c^2 \partial^2\,(rp)/\partial r^2 \qquad \ldots\,(2.25)$$

This is the general wave equation for spherical waves. Similar expressions may be obtained for y and u.

Consider a shell of radius r and thickness δr concentric with the source. By analogy with equation 2.6 we have:

$$\partial p/\partial r = -\rho \partial^2 y/\partial t^2 = -\rho \partial u/\partial t$$

Differentiating equation 2.24 with respect to r gives:

$$\partial p/\partial r = -p\,\{(1/r) + jk\}$$

Eliminating $\partial p/\partial r$ from these equations we have:

$$\partial u/\partial t = (p/\rho)\,\{(1/r) + jk\}$$

Integrating this with respect with t one then obtains:

$$u = (p/j\omega\rho)\,\{(1/r) + jk\} \qquad \ldots\,(2.26)$$

The constant of integration can be made to equal zero because

u varies sinusoidally with respect to time for all values of r and this constant will simply determine the phase of u at zero time.

The specific acoustic impedance Z_a is expressed by (see equation 2.9):

$$Z_a = p/u = j\omega\rho / \{(1/r) + jk\} = \rho ckr\,(kr + j)/(1 + k^2r^2)$$
$$\ldots\ldots(2.27)$$

This is a complex quantity; the specific acoustic resistance R_a and the specific acoustic reactance X_a are respectively given by the expressions:

$$R_a = \rho ck^2r^2/(1 + k^2r^2) \qquad \ldots\ldots(2.28)$$

$$X_a = \rho ckr/(1 + k^2r^2) \qquad \ldots\ldots(2.29)$$

It is seen that as r becomes very large compared with wavelength $\lambda = 2\pi/k$, conditions for plane waves are approached for which $R_a \longrightarrow \rho c$ and $X_a \longrightarrow 0$, i.e. spherical waves of very large radius of curvature behave very nearly as plane waves.

Let u' represent the particle velocity, p' the acoustic pressure, and Z'_a the characteristic impedance at the surface of the source. From equations 2.24 and 2.27 we have that:

$$u' = p'/Z'_a = (A/aZ'_a)\exp j\,(\omega t - ka) = u'_0\exp j\omega t$$
$$\ldots\ldots(2.30)$$

where a represents the mean radius of the source and u'_0 the amplitude of u'. Thus:

$$A = au'_0 Z'_a \exp jka$$

Where the radius a of the source is sufficiently small for $ka \ll 1$, we have that $\exp jka \longrightarrow 1$ and that:

$$Z'_a = \rho cka\,(ka + j)/(1 + k^2a^2) \mathbin{\widehat{=}} j\rho cka \qquad \ldots\ldots(2.31)$$

Hence:

$$A \mathbin{\widehat{=}} j\rho cka^2u'_0$$

25

C

PROPAGATION OF SOUND WAVES

Hence equation 2.24 may be rewritten as:

$$p = (j\rho cka^2 u'_0 / r) \exp j (\omega t - kr)$$
$$= (\rho cka^2 u'_0 / r) \exp j (\omega t - kr + \pi/2) \qquad \dots (2.32)$$

Thus the amplitude p_0 of p at a given distance r from the source is given by the expression:

$$p_0 = \rho cka^2 u'_0 / r = 2\pi\rho a^2 f u'_0 / r \qquad \dots (2.33)$$

where f is the wave frequency.

Group Velocity

Up to now we have considered what is known as the phase velocity of sound waves. In most cases this is equal to the velocity of propagation of the acoustic energy. However, cases do occur, one example being the propagation of flexural waves in bars (see Chapter 4, p. 59), where the velocity of sound varies with frequency. Thus when, in such a case, waves having more than one frequency are propagated simultaneously, the acoustic velocity is no longer the phase velocity but the velocity of the maximum amplitude of the superposed waves, i.e. the group velocity.

Consider two waves A and B having respective wavelengths λ and $\lambda + \Delta\lambda$, and respective velocities v and $v + \Delta v$, being propagated simultaneously (see *Figure 10*). At some

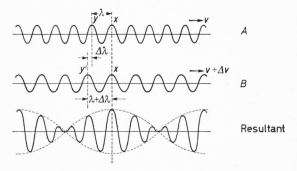

Figure 10. Simultaneous propagation of two waves having velocities v and $v + \Delta v$

time for which we make $t=0$ two peaks will be coincident at some point X at which there will be a maximum. Because the waves B are travelling faster than the waves A, at some time Δt later the adjacent peaks Y' and Y will coincide in position and the maximum will have moved back a distance λ so that the velocity of the maximum is reduced to $v - \lambda/\Delta t$. Because the distance between Y and Y' was originally $\Delta\lambda$ and the speed of approach is equal to Δv, we have $\Delta t = \Delta\lambda/\Delta v$. Hence the group velocity v_g is given by the expression:

$$v_g = v - \lambda\Delta v/\Delta\lambda \qquad \dots (2.34)$$

The Doppler Effect

The Doppler effect is responsible for an observed change in frequency when either the source of sound, the receiver, or both are in motion. The simple treatment given below considers only the most commonly met with case of the motion of the source and receiver along the same straight line.

Consider a source A travelling with a velocity u and emitting sound waves having a speed c. When the waves are travelling in the same direction as A the wavefronts are pushed closer together (see *Figure 11*) and the wavefront velocity becomes equal to $c - u$. The value of the disturbed wave-length λ' is thus given by the expression:

$$\lambda' = (c - u)/f = \lambda(1 - u/c) \qquad \dots (2.35a)$$

where f is the frequency of the emitted waves. Where the waves are travelling in the opposite direction the wavefronts are pulled further apart and the negative sign in the above expression becomes positive, i.e.,

$$\lambda' = (c + u)/f = \lambda(1 + u/c) \qquad \dots (2.35b)$$

Let an observer B be moving with a velocity v in the same direction as the motion of A. The frequency f' of the observed note from A will depend on the frequency of arrival of the wavefronts at B. Thus if the observer is moving away from the source, the relative velocity of sound is reduced to $c - v$

and fewer wavefronts arrive in a given time. The value of f' is thus decreased as given by the expression:

$$f' = (c - v)/\lambda' \qquad \dots (2.36a)$$

On the other hand, if the observer is moving towards A, the relative velocity is increased to $c + v$ and more wavefronts

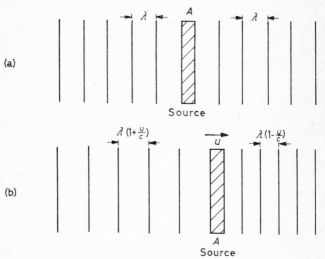

Figure 11. Effect on wave-length of a moving source

arrive at B in the same time interval. The observed frequency is thus increased and the negative sign in the above expression becomes positive, i.e.,

$$f' = (c + v)/\lambda' \qquad \dots (2.36b)$$

Eliminating λ' in the foregoing expressions, we have:

$$f' = \frac{(c \pm v)}{(c \pm u)} f = \frac{\left(1 \pm \dfrac{v}{c}\right)}{\left(1 \pm \dfrac{u}{c}\right)} f \qquad \dots (2.37)$$

28

u and v being considered as positive for motion from left to right in *Figure 11*.

The Doppler effect occurs also when the medium is moving even though both source and receiver may be stationary. In this case, although there is a change of wave-length to λ' there is no change in frequency since both u and v will be equal.

REFERENCE

[1] Newman, F. H. and Searle, V. H. L. *The General Properties of Matter,* 5th ed., p. 152, 1957. London; Arnold

FURTHER READING

Kinsler, L. E. and Frey, A. R. *Fundamentals of Acoustics.* 1950. New York; Wiley/London; Chapman and Hall

Lindsay, R. B. *Mechanical Radiation.* 1960. New York; McGraw-Hill

Morse, P. M. *Vibration and Sound,* 2nd ed. 1948. New York; McGraw-Hill

Sharman, R. V. *Vibrations and Waves.* 1963. London; Butterworths

Stephens, R. W. B. and Bate, A. E. *Wave Motion and Sound.* 1950. London; Arnold

3

REFLECTION AND DEVIATION OF SOUND WAVES

Reflection and Transmission of Plane Waves at Normal Incidence to a Plane Boundary

Consider a beam of plane waves incident normally to a plane boundary separating two semi-infinite isotropic homogeneous media 1 and 2 having characteristic impedances R_1 and R_2, respectively (see *Figure 12*). In general, part of the incident sound energy in medium 1 is reflected back along its original path and the remainder is transmitted into medium 2.

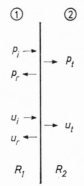

Figure 12. Acoustic pressures and particle velocities for a beam incident normally to the plane boundary between media having different characteristic impedances R_1 and R_2, respectively

Let p_i, p_r, and p_t represent values of acoustic pressure for incident, reflected, and transmitted waves, respectively, and u_i, u_r, and u_t the corresponding values of particle velocity.

REFLECTION OF PLANE WAVES

If the waves are sinusoidal in form and the medium is non-absorbent, we have:

$$p_i = A_1 \sin (\omega t - k_1 x) = u_i R_1 \qquad \dots (3.1)$$

$$p_r = B_1 \sin (\omega t + k_1 x) = - u_r R_1 \qquad \dots (3.2)$$

$$p_t = A_2 \sin (\omega t - k_2 x) = u_t R_2 \qquad \dots (3.3)$$

The symbols A_1, B_1, and A_2 represent pressure amplitudes, and k_1 and k_2 the wave numbers $2\pi/\lambda$ for the media; x is considered positive in the direction of the incident beam. In equation 3.2 the changes in sign for x and R_1 indicate that the reflected wave travels in the negative direction of x, for which c must be negative.

At the boundary the following conditions must be obeyed at all times: (a) to preserve continuity the pressure must be the same on both sides, i.e.,

$$p_t = p_i + p_r \qquad \dots (3.4)$$

(b) particle velocities directed normally to the boundary must be equal on both sides otherwise the two media would no longer remain in contact with one another, i.e.,

$$u_t = u_i + u_r \qquad \dots (3.5)$$

At the boundary, which we shall consider as the origin, $x = 0$ and the equations 3.4 and 3.5 thus become:

$$A_2 = A_1 + B_1 \qquad \dots (3.6)$$

and

$$R_1 A_2 = R_2 (A_1 - B_1) \qquad \dots (3.7)$$

Thus

$$p_t / p_i = A_2 / A_1 = 2R_2 / (R_1 + R_2) \qquad \dots (3.8)$$

and

$$p_r / p_i = B_1 / A_1 = (R_2 - R_1) / (R_1 + R_2) \qquad \dots (3.9)$$

Also

$$u_t / u_i = A_2 R_1 / A_1 R_2 = 2R_1 / (R_1 + R_2) \qquad \dots (3.10)$$

and

$$u_r / u_i = - B_1 / A_1 = (R_1 - R_2) / (R_1 + R_2) \qquad \dots (3.11)$$

Where R_2 is greater than R_1, i.e., for sound travelling from an acoustically less dense medium to an acoustically denser medium (e.g., from air to a solid), equation 3.9 shows that reflection takes place without any change in phase of acoustic pressure, whereas equation 3.11 shows that a 180 degree phase change occurs in particle velocity and, hence, particle displacement.

At the boundary, the ratio of the acoustic intensity of the reflected waves to that of the incident waves defines the reflection coefficient α_r, and the ratio of the intensity of the transmitted waves to that of the incident waves is called the transmission coefficient α_t. Equations 3.9 and 3.11 thus give:

$$\alpha_r = (R_2 - R_1)^2 / (R_1 + R_2)^2 \qquad \dots (3.12)$$

and equations 3.8 and 3.10 give

$$\alpha_t = 4R_1 R_2 / (R_1 + R_2)^2 \qquad \dots (3.13)$$

These equations show that, where R_1 and R_2 are equal, α_t reaches its maximum value of unity and α_r becomes equal to zero. This represents the ideal case of perfect acoustic coupling between the two media but, in practice, good coupling will occur when R_1 and R_2 have values of the same order of magnitude, i.e., α_t has a value of greater than 10 per cent. Coupling is poor when one of the media is a gas and the other a solid or liquid, for which α_t may be less than 0·01 per cent. Values of α_t can be calculated from the characteristic impedances listed in Table 1. It can be seen, for example, that the transmission coefficient for longitudinal waves passing from steel to air or vice versa is about 10^{-6}; i.e., the reflection coefficient is virtually unity.

The conditions for reflection and transmission can be considerably altered if a parallel layer of a third medium is placed between the two media. If the characteristic impedance of this intervening medium is equal to R', it can be shown, see, for example, Kinsler and Frey[1], page 152, that:

$$\alpha_t = 4R_1 R_2 / \{(R_1 + R_2)^2 \cos^2 k'l + (R' + R_1 R_2 / R')^2 \sin^2 k'l\}$$
$$\dots (3.14)$$

where k' is the wave number for third medium.

Three special cases may be considered:

(a) Where the intervening medium is sufficiently thin that

REFLECTION OF PLANE WAVES

$k'l \ll 1$, the cosine term in equation 3.14 tends to unity and the sine term becomes negligible. The expression then reduces to equation 3.13 and the intervening medium should then have no effect on the transmission of sound. The value of l required to satisfy this condition depends on the values of

Table 1. Characteristic Impedances for Some Commonly Used Materials*

Material	Longitudinal wave velocity c msec^{-1}	Density ρ g cm^{-3}	Characteristic impedance ρc kg m^{-2} sec^{-1}
Aluminium	6,400	2·7	$1·7 \times 10^7$
Brass	3,500	8·6	$3·0 \times 10^7$
Copper	4,700	8·9	$4·2 \times 10^7$
Gold	3,700	10·5	$3·9 \times 10^7$
Iron	5,900	7·9	$4·7 \times 10^7$
Lead	1,200	11·3	$1·4 \times 10^7$
Nickel	5,600	8·9	$5·0 \times 10^7$
Platinum	3,900	21·45	$8·4 \times 10^7$
Silver	3,200	19·3	$6·2 \times 10^7$
Steel	6,000	7·8	$4·7 \times 10^7$
Barium titanate	5,000	5·4	$2·7 \times 10^7$
Quartz (X-cut)	5,700	2·6	$1·5 \times 10^7$
Nylon	2,700	1·14	$3·0 \times 10^6$
Perspex (Lucite)	2,700	1·2	$3·2 \times 10^6$
Glycerol	1,900	1·26	$2·4 \times 10^6$
Lubricating oil (approximate values)	1,400	0·8	$1·1 \times 10^6$
Olive oil	1,400	0·9	$1·3 \times 10^6$
Water	1,500	1·0	$1·5 \times 10^6$
Air	330	0·0013	430
Hydrogen	1,300	0·00090	110
Oxygen	320	0·0014	450

*The values quoted are for room temperatures and have been obtained mainly from Kaye and Laby[4] (by courtesy of Longmans Green) and the *Handbook of Chemistry and Physics*[5] (by courtesy of the Chemical Rubber Company).

R_1R_2/R' and k' and, hence, on the frequency. Thus a thin solid sheet in air may transmit waves of audio frequencies but would act as a reflector of ultrasonic waves.

(b) Where the thickness of the intervening medium is an integral number of half wave-lengths, i.e., $l=n\lambda/2$ or $k'l=n\pi$, equation 3.14 again reduces to equation 3.13.

(c) Where the thickness of the intervening medium is equal to an odd number of quarter wave-lengths, i.e., $l=(2n-1)\lambda/4$ or $k'l=(2n-1)\pi/2$, equation 3.14 reduces to the following expression:

$$\alpha_t = 4R_1R_2/(R' + R_1R_2/R')^2 \qquad \dots (3.15)$$

Thus 100 per cent transmission will occur when $R'^2 = R_1R_2$. It is assumed here that flexural vibrations do not occur at the boundaries, in which case the conditions may be altered considerably (see Chapter 7).

Reflection at Oblique Incidence, and Refraction

Consider a parallel beam of longitudinal plane waves incident obliquely to a plane boundary separating media 1 and 2 and let XY (see *Figure 13*) represent a ray of such a beam, Y being the point of incidence at the boundary. YW and YZ are the respective reflected and refracted longitudinal waves. Where one or both the media support a shear stress, mode conversion will take place at the boundary. This is because the acoustic pressure due to the incident beam is directed obliquely to the boundary and can consequently be resolved into components perpendicular to and parallel with it. The layers of media in the vicinity of the boundary thus suffer both compressional and shear stresses. This means that shear waves as well as compression waves may be reflected and transmitted, as indicated by YW' and YZ', respectively, in *Figure 13*.

The velocities and directions of the different waves are given, in accordance with Snell's law, by the expression:

$$c_1/\sin\theta_1 = c'_1/\sin\theta'_1 = c_2/\sin\theta_2 = c'_2/\sin\theta'_2$$
$$\dots (3.16)$$

Here c_1 and c_2 represent the longitudinal wave velocities in media 1 and 2, respectively, and c_1' and c_2' represent the corresponding shear wave velocities. θ_1 represents the angle of incidence and also that of reflection, to which it is equal. θ_2 represents the angle of refraction for the longitudinal

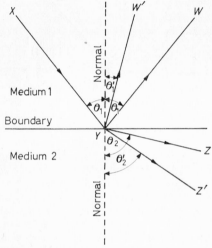

Figure 13. Reflection and refraction of a beam of longitudinal waves incident to a plane boundary separating two media

waves and θ_1' and θ_2' represent, respectively, the angles of reflection and refraction for the shear waves.

Supposing that medium 1 is a fluid and medium 2 a solid, for which c_1 is less than both c_2 and c_2'. Equation 3.16 shows that both transmitted rays are refracted away from the normal. Furthermore, because the shear wave velocity must be less than the compression wave velocity, θ_2 is always greater than θ_2'. Let the angle of incidence be increased to its first critical value for which the refracted longitudinal ray YZ is directed along the boundary, i.e. $\theta_2 = 90$ degrees (see *Figure 14a*). For angles of incidence greater than this, the longitudinal waves are totally reflected and only shear waves are transmitted through the solid. When the angle θ_1 is increased to its second critical value, the refracted transverse waves are then directed along the boundary and become surface waves (see *Figure 14b*).

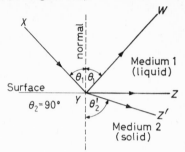

(a) θ_1 equal to its first critical value

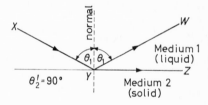

(b) θ_1 equal to its second critical value

Figure 14. The propagation of (a) shear waves and (b) surface waves as the result of the incidence of longitudinal waves to a liquid–solid boundary

Stationary Waves
General Considerations

Where plane waves are reflected at normal incidence to a plane boundary, as discussed at the beginning of this chapter, the incident and reflected waves in medium 1 will interfere with one another to form stationary or standing waves. The resultant acoustic pressure p at any point in this medium is given by the expression:

$$p = p_i + p_r$$

and the corresponding particle velocity u by the equation:

$$u = u_i + u_r$$

If we assume that the medium is non-absorptive we have, from equations 3.1 and 3.2:

$$p = A \sin(\omega t - kx) + B \sin(\omega t + kx)$$

and

$$u = (A/R_1) \sin(\omega t - kx) - (B/R_1) \sin(\omega t + kx)$$

where, for convenience, the suffix 1 has been dropped from A, B, and k. Putting p_0 as the pressure amplitude and u_0 as the particle velocity amplitude for the incident waves, and $r = B/A$ for which $r^2 = \alpha_r$, we have that $A = p_0$ and $B = rp_0$. Hence:

$$p = p_0 \sin(\omega t - kx) + rp_0 \sin(\omega t + kx) \quad \dots (3.17)$$

and

$$u = u_0 \sin(\omega t - kx) - ru_0 \sin(\omega t + kx) \quad \dots (3.18)$$

The following two cases are now considered:

(i) R_2 is Greater than R_1

Equation 3.9 shows that there is no change in phase on reflection for p and equation 3.11 shows that there is a 180 degree phase change on reflection for u. Thus in equations 3.17 and 3.18, $r = B/A$ is positive; the equations may consequently be rewritten in the following forms:

$$p = 2rp_0 \cos kx \sin \omega t + (1-r) p_0 \sin(\omega t - kx)$$
$$\dots (3.19)$$

$$u = 2ru_0 \sin kx \cos \omega t + (1-r) u_0 \sin(\omega t - kx)$$
$$\dots (3.20)$$

The values of the resultant pressure amplitude P and particle velocity amplitude U depend on the value of x; variations of these are illustrated in *Figure 15*. At the boundary, where $x = 0$, and at distances from it of integral numbers n of half wave-lengths, for which $x = -n\lambda/2$, i.e., $kx = -n\pi$, equations 3.17 and 3.18 show that:

$$p = \pm p_0 (1+r) \sin \omega t = \pm P \sin \omega t$$

37

or $\qquad P = p_0 (1 + r) = P_{max.}$ $\qquad \dots (3.21)$

and $\qquad u = \pm u_0 (1 - r) \sin \omega t = \pm U \sin \omega t$

or $\qquad U = u_0 (1 - r) = U_{min.}$ $\qquad \dots (3.22)$

i.e., the pressure amplitude is a maximum and the velocity amplitude is a minimum.

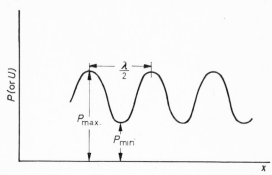

Figure 15. Variation of pressure amplitude (or particle velocity amplitude) with distance in a stationary wave system

On the other hand, at distances of odd numbers of quarter wave-lengths from the boundary, for which $x = -(2n - 1)\lambda/4$, i.e., $kx = -(2n - 1) \pi/2$, we have that:

$$p = \pm p_0 (1 - r) \cos \omega t = \pm P \cos \omega t$$

or $\qquad P = p_0 (1 - r) = P_{min.}$ $\qquad \dots (3.23)$

and $\qquad u = \pm u_0 (1 + r) \cos \omega t = \pm U \cos \omega t$

or $\qquad U = u_0 (1 + r) = U_{max.}$ $\qquad \dots (3.24)$

i.e., the pressure amplitude is a minimum and the velocity amplitude is a maximum.

In the special case where total reflection occurs at the boundary, $r = 1$ and it is seen that $P_{max.} = 2p_0$, $P_{min.} = 0$, $U_{max.} = 2u_0$, and $U_{min.} = 0$. Positions of zero amplitude are called nodes and of maximum amplitude are termed anti-nodes.

(ii) R_2 is Less than R_1

In this case equation 3.11 predicts a 180 degree phase change for p and no phase change for u. Thus r becomes negative in equations 3.17 and 3.18, and we have that:

$$p = 2rp_0 \sin kx \cos \omega t + (1 - r) p_0 \sin (\omega t - kx)$$
.... (3.25)

and

$$u = 2ru_0 \cos kx \sin \omega t + (1 - r) u_0 \sin (\omega t - kx)$$
.... (3.26)

Following the same argument given in the previous sub-section, it is seen that at the boundary and at distances of integral numbers of half wave-lengths from it, $P = P_{\min.}$ and $U = U_{\max.}$. At distances of odd numbers of quarter wave-lengths from the boundary $P = P_{\max.}$ and $U = U_{\min.}$. As before, nodes will be observed when the reflection coefficient is 100 per cent.

It is left as an exercise for the reader to show that maxima and minima of particle displacement amplitude will occur at the positions of maxima and minima, respectively, of particle velocity amplitude.

Stationary Wave Ratio

The ratio of maximum to minimum amplitude in a stationary wave system is described by the term stationary (or standing) wave ratio (SWR) as defined by the expression:

$$\text{SWR} = P_{\max.}/P_{\min.} = U_{\max.}/U_{\min.} = (1 + r)/(1 - r)$$
.... (3.27)

This quantity varies from infinity, for which there is total reflection, to unity, for which there is no reflection and the waves are thus purely progressive.

Resonance of a Stationary Wave System

General

When stationary waves are formed in a medium terminated at each end by parallel boundaries perpendicular to the wave motion (see p. 32), one can regard the medium, as a whole, as undergoing forced vibrations due to the action of the sound waves. The natural frequency will be dependent on the total length of the stationary wave system and also on whether or not phase changes take place on reflection at the ends. Resonance (see Chapter 1, p. 12) will occur in some cases where the length of the medium is an integral number of half wave-lengths and in other cases where it is an odd number of quarter wave-lengths.

Half Wave-Length Resonance

Half wave-length resonance occurs when the phase change on reflection is the same at both ends of the system. This means that the medium will be terminated by two maximum or two minimum amplitudes and, in the special case of total reflection at both ends, by either two nodes or two antinodes. Thus a solid rod surrounded by air will have particle velocity antinodes, particle displacement antinodes, and pressure nodes at its ends and so will a column of gas contained in a tube open at both ends. In the latter case reflection takes place at the end of the tube as a result of discontinuity. On the other hand, particle velocity nodes, particle displacement nodes, and pressure antinodes are to be found at the ends of a column of gas enclosed in a tube closed at both ends or a flexible string stretched between two fixed supports.

The length l of the system is equal to an integral number n of half wave-lengths, as given by:

$$l = n\lambda/2 \qquad \dots (3.28a)$$

The resonant or natural frequency f of the system will be given by the expression:

$$f = c/\lambda = nc/2l \qquad \dots (3.28b)$$

The lowest of the natural frequencies, for which $n = 1$, is called the fundamental and the others, for which n is greater than unity, are called harmonics or partials, the orders of which are given by the values of n. Thus the first overtone, for which $n = 2$, is called the second harmonic. It should be possible to excite all of the harmonics of a half wave-length resonant system. However, one can suppress certain of the

40

harmonics by such means as clamping the vibrating body at an antinode. In general, it will be observed that the amplitude diminishes with the increase of the order of the harmonic and it may prove to be extremely difficult to excite very high orders.

Quarter Wave-Length Resonance

Quarter wave-length resonance will be observed when there is no change in phase at one end of a stationary wave system and a phase change of 180 degrees at the other end of it. This can occur for a solid clamped at one end to provide a node and left free at the other end to provide an antinode. It can also occur for a column of gas in a tube closed at one end and open at the other.

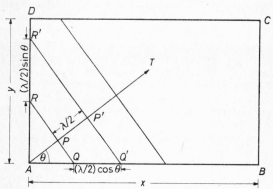

Figure 16. Propagation of plane waves in a rectangular plate

Resonance will be observed when the length of the system is equal to an odd number of quarter wave-lengths, as given by the expression:

$$l = (2n-1) \lambda/4 \qquad \ldots (3.29a)$$

The corresponding natural frequency is given by the equation:

$$f = c/\lambda = (2n-1) c/4l \qquad \ldots (3.29b)$$

It can be seen that only the fundamental frequency and odd harmonics can be excited.

41

D

Quality of Resonance

In the ideal case where the reflection coefficient at both ends of the system is unity and the medium is non-absorbent, thus giving a stationary wave ratio of infinity, perfect nodes will occur at the positions of the minimum amplitudes. The waves will then be reflected backwards and forwards without loss of energy and the amplitude at the antinodes will eventually build up to infinity, i.e., the mechanical Q factor (see Chapter 1, p. 13) will be equal to infinity. This does not happen in practice because both reflection and absorption losses will always occur. The value of the Q factor will thus vary with the stationary wave ratio.

Timbre

If vibrations are excited by a disturbance having a continuous range of frequencies, e.g., by blowing across the mouth of a column of air such as an organ pipe, by striking a rod, or by plucking a stretched string, the notes which will be heard are those having resonant frequencies, i.e., the fundamental and harmonics. The relative strengths of the harmonics are characteristic of the properties of the medium; this explains why that a note of given pitch differs in musical quality, or timbre, when emitted from different musical instruments. The timbre of a note can be changed by the suppression of certain harmonics, e.g., for a violin by placing the finger on the string to suppress an antinode. When an organ pipe, open at both ends, is stopped by closing one of the ends there is a halving of frequency and a change in timbre due to the conversion of an open tube to a closed tube. The resultant motion of any part of the system can be obtained from Fourier's equation (see Chapter 1, p. 6).

In Chapter 4, p. 57, a short account is given of the transverse vibrations of rods and plates for which the velocity varies with frequency. In such cases the overtones are no longer harmonics of the fundamental frequency.

Stationary Waves in Two and Three Dimensions

In the previous section the formation of stationary waves in one dimension only was considered. We shall now present a brief account of the formation of these waves in both two and three dimensions for which plane waves are incident at some oblique angle to the boundaries of the system.

Two-Dimensional Stationary Waves

Examples of two-dimensional systems include thin plates and membranes. Let $ABCD$ (*Figure 16*) represent a rectangular plate and suppose that waves are travelling along its surface in a direction AT at some angle θ to AB. Let QPR represent a straight line joining all points in the wave having the same phase and let $Q'P'R'$ represent a similar straight line parallel with QPR and at a distance of one half wavelength from it. Thus the lengths of the intercepts on the sides AB and AD are $(\lambda/2)/\cos\theta$ and $(\lambda/2)/\sin\theta$, respectively, λ representing the wave-length.

Resonance occurs when $AB = x = (n_1\lambda/2)/\cos\theta$ and $AD = y = (n_2\lambda/2)/\sin\theta$, where n_1 and n_2 are integers. Thus:

$$(n_1\lambda/2x)^2 + (n_2\lambda/2y)^2 = \sin^2\theta + \cos^2\theta = 1$$

or

$$\{(n_1/x)^2 + (n_2/y)^2\}^{\frac{1}{2}} = 2/\lambda \qquad \ldots (3.30a)$$

The value of the corresponding resonant frequency f is given by the expression:

$$f = (c/2)\{(n_1/x)^2 + (n_2/y)^2\}^{\frac{1}{2}} \qquad \ldots (3.30b)$$

Three-Dimensional Stationary Waves

For a rectangular prism having dimensions x, y, and z it can be shown using the method of the previous section that for resonance:

$$\{(n_1/x)^2 + (n_2/y)^2 + (n_3/z)^2\}^{\frac{1}{2}} = 2/\lambda \quad \ldots (3.31a)$$

for which the resonant frequency is given by the equation:

$$f = (c/2)\{(n_1/x)^2 + (n_2/y)^2 + (n_3/z)^2\}^{\frac{1}{2}} \ldots (3.31b)$$

The resonant frequencies are sometimes called eigentones.

Diffraction and Scattering

General Considerations

Diffraction or bending is a property of wave motion which occurs when waves are passed through an aperture or when they are obstructed by some object placed in their path. Diffraction is also associated with the finite size of a source. It occurs with both sound and light waves but because of the longer wave-lengths it is more readily observed with sound waves. When the dimensions of an obstacle in a beam are small compared with wave-length, scattering of the waves will take place.

Diffraction Due to a Circular Source

Consider a plane circular source of sound vibrating with simple harmonic motion in a piston-like manner, i.e., all points on the radiating surface are in phase with one another. The source is assumed to be located in an infinite baffle and one need consider only waves radiated from one of the surfaces. If it is assumed that the source consists of a very large number of small spherical sources on its surface, all vibrating in phase at the same frequency and amplitude, it can be shown, see for example Kinsler and Frey[1], page 185, that the intensity I_0 at some point along the axis, distance r from the source is expressed as follows:

$$I_0 = 2\rho c u_0^2 \sin^2 (k/2) \{(r^2 + a^2)^{\frac{1}{2}} - r\} \qquad \ldots . (3.32)$$

where u_0 represents the velocity amplitude of the source, a the radius of the source, ρ the density of the medium, and $k = 2\pi/\lambda$, where λ represents the wave-length.

The variation of I_0 with r as given by equation 3.32 is illustrated in *Figure 17*. It is seen that the value of I_0 passes through a number of maxima each having the same value $I_{max.}$ and through zero minima. The last maximum occurs at a point A at a distance $r = a^2/\lambda$ from the source. Beyond A, where r is sufficiently large compared with a, the sinusoidal term in equation 3.32 is small and the equation reduces to the form:

$$I_0 = \rho c k^2 a^4 u_0^2 / 8r^2 \qquad \ldots . (3.33)$$

i.e., the value of I_0 falls off with distance from the source in accordance with the inverse square law.

The region between the source and the cross-section through

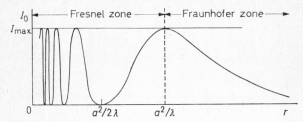

Figure 17. Variation of intensity along the axis of a circular source vibrating as a piston in an infinite baffle

A is called the Fresnel or near zone and the region beyond A is known as the Fraunhofer or far zone. In the Fresnel zone, where the intensity varies between maximum and minimum values, the waves are plane so that the beam is thus parallel; in the Fraunhofer zone the beam is divergent, appearing to originate from the centre of the source.

Equation 3.31 predicts the alternating variation of intensity along the axis in the Fresnel zone, but if one integrates the intensity over a complete cross-section it is found, as expected from a consideration of the principle of conservation of energy, that the rate of flow of energy is constant for all cross-sections. Thus the variation of intensity with distance will differ along lines parallel with the axis.

In addition to the main beam, a number of side lobes will often be observed in the Fraunhofer zone. It can be shown (see, for example, Kinsler and Frey[1], page 183) that the value of the intensity I, at some point P off the axis, in comparison with that of the axial intensity I_0, as given by equation 3.33, at the same distance from the centre of the source is given by the expression:

$$I = \{4J_1^2 \, (ka \sin \theta)/(ka \sin \theta)^2\} \, I_0 \qquad \ldots \ldots (3.34)$$

where θ is the angle subtended to the centre of the source by the radius vector of P and the axis. $J_1 \, (ka \sin \theta)$ is a Bessel's function of the first order (see, for example, Sokolnikoff[2]), the value of which can be obtained from tables.

Figure 18 contains polar diagrams showing how intensity varies in front of a piston-like circular source, for different values of a/λ. It is seen that the greater the value of a/λ (or

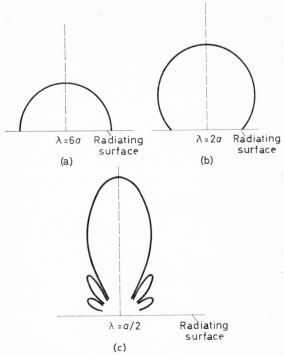

Figure 18. Polar diagrams of intensity for a beam radiating from a piston source in an infinite baffle, for different values of radius a and wave-length λ

ka), for which either the frequency is higher or the source is larger, the greater the directivity of the beam and the higher the number of side lobes. The value of θ for the first minimum, as given by equation 3.34, is $0.61\,\lambda/a$, i.e., the angular width of the main beam is $1 \cdot 22 \lambda / a$. Most of the energy is contained in the main beam; the amount of energy in the side lobes is very small indeed.

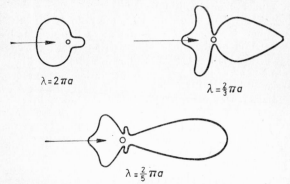

Figure 19. *Polar diagrams of intensity for a beam scattered from a cylindrical obstacle, for different values of radius a and wave-length λ*

(From *Vibration and Sound*, by P. M. Morse[3]. Copyright 1948. McGraw-Hill Book Company. Used by permission.)

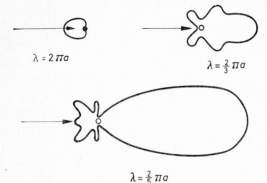

Figure 20. *Polar diagrams of intensity for a beam scattered from a spherical obstacle, for different values of radius a and wave-length λ*

(From *Vibration and Sound*, by P. M. Morse[3]. Copyright 1948. McGraw-Hill Book Company. Used by permission.)

47

REFLECTION OF SOUND WAVES

Scattering of Sound by Small Obstacles

A small obstacle is regarded for our purpose as being either cylindrical in shape (e.g., a microphone stand) or spherical (e.g., a microphone housing).

Expressions may be obtained for the ratio of the intensity of a scattered beam of sound to that of the incident beam as a function of the angle of scattering (see, for example, Morse[3], page 346). These expressions are complicated in form and, in a book of this level of treatment, it is best to represent the relationships in the forms of polar diagrams, see *Figures 19* and *20*. Where, for a spherical obstacle, the radius is small compared with wave-length ($\lambda > 2\pi a$ in *Figure 20*) the amount of energy lost increases in proportion to the fourth power of the frequency. This is known as Rayleigh scattering, which is responsible for the attenuation of ultrasonic waves by small particles in suspension in fluids and by the grain structure in polycrystalline solids.

REFERENCES

[1] Kinsler, L. E. and Frey, A. R. *Fundamentals of Acoustics.* 1950. New York; Wiley/London; Chapman and Hall

[2] Sokolnikoff, I. S. and Sokolnikoff, E. S. *Higher Mathematics for Engineers and Physicists,* 2nd ed., p. 332. 1941. New York; McGraw-Hill

[3] Morse, P. M. *Vibration and Sound,* 2nd ed. 1948. New .. York; McGraw-Hill

[4] Kaye, G. W. C. and Laby, T. H. *Tables of Physical and Chemical Constants,* 11th ed. 1957. London; Longmans Green

[5] *Handbook of Chemistry and Physics* (published annually). Cleveland, Ohio; Chemical Rubber Company

THE VELOCITY AND ABSORPTION OF SOUND WAVES

Velocities in Fluids Having Large Areas of Cross-Section

When a compression wave is passed through an unbounded medium the volume elements of the medium are subjected to alternating stresses, each having two components. One of these is a uniform compressional stress and the other a shear stress. Because a fluid will not normally support a shear stress the result will be a uniform compression only and the appropriate modulus to be substituted in equation 2.8 is the bulk modulus K. Thus

$$c = (K/\rho)^{\frac{1}{2}} \qquad \dots (4.1)$$

where ρ is the density and c the velocity of longitudinal waves. It should be mentioned that it is possible to propagate shear waves for very short distances in highly viscous and viscoelastic liquids (see, for example, Blitz[1], page 127). Tables 2 and 3 give values of acoustic velocities in a number of liquids and gases.

For an ideal gas it can easily be shown (see, for example, Newman and Searle[2], page 150) that the adiabatic bulk modulus is equal to γP, where γ is the ratio of the specific heat at constant pressure to the specific heat at constant volume and P is the static pressure of the gas. At room temperatures gases such as air, oxygen, nitrogen, and hydrogen have properties which approximate very closely to those of an ideal gas, for which the velocity of sound is given by the expression:

$$c = (\gamma P/\rho)^{\frac{1}{2}} \qquad \dots (4.2)$$

Table 2. Acoustic Velocities in Liquids at 20°C

Liquid	Velocity msec^{-1}
Acetone	1,200
Benzene	1,320
Carbon tetrachloride	950
Castor oil	1,500
Chlorobenzene	1,320
Ethyl alcohol	1,200
Glycerol (pure)	1,940
Methyl alcohol	1,120
Nitrobenzene	1,480
Olive oil	1,440
Toluene	1,320
Water	1,490

Table 3. Acoustic Velocities in Gases at s.t.p.

Gas	Velocity msec^{-1}
Air	330
Argon	320
Carbon dioxide	260
Helium	970
Hydrogen	1,300
Neon	430
Nitrogen	330
Oxygen	310

If one substitutes the equation of state for an ideal gas, namely,

$$PV = rT$$

into equation 4.2, where $V = 1/\rho$ is the volume of 1 g of the gas, T the absolute temperature, and r is a constant for a given gas, we have:

$$c = (\gamma rT)^{\frac{1}{2}} \qquad \dots (4.3)$$

Because γ and r are constants for a given gas under normal conditions, it is seen from equation 4.3 that the velocity of sound varies directly with the square root of the absolute temperature. Let c_0 represent the velocity of sound at $0°$ C; because $T = 273 + t$, we have that:

$$c = c_0 (1 + t/273)^{\frac{1}{2}} \qquad \ldots (4.4)$$

It is seen that the velocity varies with temperature only and is thus independent of the pressure of the gas. This may not be the case where the pressure is very high or very low or for high ultrasonic frequencies.

Where two gases are mixed together, the velocity of sound in the mixture varies linearly with the relative masses. For liquids this is so only where both liquids mixed together are unassociated. One would thus expect that the velocity in a fluid is affected by the presence of impurities. A well-known example is the effect of the presence of water vapour in air; a correction for relative humidity must thus be made to the value of the velocity of sound in air.

Velocities in Solids Having Large Areas of Cross-Section

When a portion of a solid in bulk is subjected to a compression, it suffers a uniform compressional stress and also a shear stress. It is thus to be expected that the elastic modulus will contain a rigidity component. It can be shown (see, for example, Newman and Searle[2], page 396) that the elastic modulus is equal to $K + 4G/3$, which is equivalent to $Y(1 - \sigma)/(1 + \sigma)(1 - 2\sigma)$, where G represents the shear modulus, Y the Young's modulus, and σ the Poisson's ratio. The velocity of longitudinal or compression waves in a solid in bulk is thus given by the expression:

$$c = \{(K + 4G/3)/\rho\}^{\frac{1}{2}} = \{Y(1 - \sigma)/\rho(1 + \sigma)(1 - 2\sigma)\}^{\frac{1}{2}} \qquad \ldots (4.5)$$

When alternating shear stresses are applied to a solid in bulk form, shear or transverse waves are propagated. The value c_s of the shear velocity is given by the expression:

$$c_s = (G/\rho)^{\frac{1}{2}} \qquad \ldots (4.6)$$

Table 4. Values of Elastic Moduli and Acoustic Velocities for Some Metals in Polycrystalline Form*

| Metal | Young's modulus Y newtons m^{-2} ×10^{-10} | Bulk modulus K newtons m^{-2} ×10^{-10} | Rigidity G newtons m^{-2} ×10^{-10} | Density ρ g cm^{-3} | Velocity of longitudinal waves | | Velocity of shear waves msec^{-1} |
					Solids in bulk msec^{-1}	Rods msec^{-1}	
Aluminium (worked)	7·05	7·46	2·63	2·7	6,400	5,100	3,100
Copper	12·3	13·1	4·55	8·9	4,700	3,700	1,200
Gold	8·0	16·6	2·80	19·3	3,200	2,000	1,200
Iron	21·3	16·1	8·31	7·9	5,900	5,200	3,200
Lead	1·62	5·0	0·56	11·3	2,300	1,200	790
Nickel	20·2	17·6	7·7	8·9	5,600	4,800	2,900
Platinum	16·8	24·7	6·04	21·45	3,900	2,800	1,700
Silver	7·9	10·9	2·86	10·5	3,700	2,700	1,600
Steel (worked)	20·9	16·4	8·12	7·8	6,000	5,200	2,900
Tin	5·43	5·29	2·04	7·3	3,300	2,700	1,700

*The velocities were calculated from values of elastic constants given by Kaye and Laby[3] (by courtesy of Longmans Green).

52

Table 4 contains values of longitudinal and shear wave velocities in a number of isotropic solids in bulk form. It is seen that for a given solid the shear wave velocity is roughly half the compression wave velocity. Most single crystals display anisotropy, i.e., the values of its elastic constants vary with direction; consequently the acoustic velocities will also change with direction. Also, in some cases it will be found that the shear wave velocity in a given direction will depend on the polarization, i.e., the direction of the particle displacement.

It is also possible to generate surface waves in a solid, these being directed along the surface of the medium; one method of doing this is explained in Chapter 3, p. 36. In general there are two types of surface waves, these being known respectively as Love waves and Rayleigh waves. Love waves are transverse waves polarized in the plane of the surface. The polarization of Rayleigh waves has two components, one being transverse at right-angles to the plane of the surface and the other being longitudinal.

Velocities of Longitudinal Waves in Media Having Finite Areas of Cross-Section

Solid Rods and Bars

When longitudinal waves are propagated along the axis of a solid rod having cross-sectional dimensions comparable with or smaller than the wave-length, the lateral boundaries will not exert a reaction to the applied compressional stresses. The appropriate elastic modulus is then the Young's modulus Y, and the acoustic velocity c is given by the expression:

$$c = (Y/\rho)^{\frac{1}{2}} \qquad \dots (4.7)$$

Values of velocities in rods are always lower than those for the same solids in bulk form (see Table 4).

Fluids Contained in Tubes of Uniform Bore

When a fluid is contained in a tube having a diameter comparable with or smaller than the wave-length the effect of the walls of the tube must be taken into account. First of all the mechanical friction between the surface of the tube and the fluid (i.e., the viscosity) will reduce the motion of the particles and, secondly, heat exchanges between the tube walls and the fluid tend to upset the adiabatic conditions which are experienced by free fluids. Both these effects contribute towards a reduction in velocity. It has been shown (see Wood[3]) that the velocity v in a gas contained in a tube and the velocity c in the same gas when free are related as follows:

$$v = c \left\{ 1 - k'/2r \, (\pi f)^{\frac{1}{2}} \right\} \qquad \ldots . (4.8)$$

where r is the radius of the tube, f the frequency, and k' a quantity which is constant for a given fluid under specified physical conditions. For air at normal temperatures k' has a numerical value of about 0·6, where the lengths are measured in metres.

Propagation in Horns
General Considerations

Consider waves propagated in a horn in the direction shown in *Figure 21* and let AB represent a thin parallel-sided layer, perpendicular to the direction of the waves, of thickness δx and distance x from some origin. Let S represent the area of the surface A and let $F = pS$ be the acoustic force acting on A.

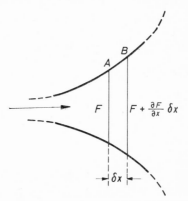

Figure 21. Forces acting on a layer of air in a horn due to the passage of sound waves

The force acting on B is $F + (\partial F/\partial x)\,\delta x$ (cf. Chapter 2, p. 19). Thus the excess force acting on the layer causing it to move is given, from Newton's Second Law, by the expression:

$$-(\partial F/\partial x)\,\delta x = \rho S\,(\partial^2 y/\partial t^2)\,\delta x \qquad \ldots (4.9)$$

where y represents the particle displacement, assuming that S remains constant over the very short distance δx.

Now, from equations 2.5 and 2.8, we have that

$$p = -\rho c^2 \partial y/\partial x$$

Hence: $\quad \partial F/\partial x = \partial\,(pS)/\partial x = S\partial p/\partial x + p\partial S/\partial x$

i.e. $\quad \partial F/\partial x = -\rho c^2\,[S\partial^2 y/\partial x^2 + (\partial y/\partial x)\,(\partial S/\partial x)] \quad \ldots (4.10)$

Thus, from equations 4.9 and 4.10 we have:

$$\partial^2 y/\partial t^2 = c^2\,\{\partial^2 y/\partial x^2 + (1/S)\,(\partial S/\partial x)\,\partial y/\partial x\}$$

i.e. $\quad \partial^2 y/\partial t^2 = c^2\,\{\partial^2 y/\partial x^2 + (\partial y/\partial x)\partial \log_e S/\partial x\} \quad \ldots (4.11)$

The plane wave equation 2.4 is thus modified by the addition of the second term in the right-hand side of equation 4.11.

Two types of horn will be considered, namely the conical horn and the exponential horn.

The Conical Horn

Let l be the length of the cone and let S_0 be the area of cross-section at the mouth. It is assumed that the area of the throat is negligible. Thus we have that:

$$S/S_0 = x^2/l^2$$

i.e. $\quad \log_e S = 2 \log_e x + \log_e (S_0/l^2)$

and $\quad \partial \log_e S/\partial x = 2/x$

Substituting this expression into equation 4.11 we have:

$$\partial^2 y/\partial t^2 = c^2\,\{\partial^2 y/\partial x^2 + (2/x)\,\partial y/\partial x\} \quad \ldots (4.12)$$

which can be written as:

$$\partial^2\,(xy)/\partial t^2 = c^2 \partial^2\,(xy)/\partial x^2 \qquad \ldots (4.13)$$

This is similar in form to equation 2.25. Hence, provided that the throat is small, spherical waves are propagated in a conical horn with a velocity c, attenuation of intensity being in accordance with the inverse square law.

The Exponential Horn

The cross-sectional area S of an exponential horn varies as:

$$S = S_0 \exp mx$$

where S_0 represents the area of cross-section of the throat and m is called the flare constant. This relationship may be written as follows:

$$\log_e S = \log_e S_0 + mx$$

Thus

$$\partial (\log_e S) / \partial x = m$$

and the wave equation 4.11 may then be written as:

$$\partial^2 y / \partial t^2 = c^2 (\partial^2 y / \partial x^2 + m \partial y / \partial x) \qquad \dots (4.14)$$

The solution of this equation for progressive waves is:

$$y = A \exp (-\alpha x) \exp j (\omega t - k'x) \qquad \dots (4.15)$$

where A is constant,

$$\alpha = m/2, \ k' = (k^2 - m^2/4)^{\frac{1}{2}}, \text{ and } k = 2\pi/\lambda = \omega/c.$$

The velocity v is then given by the expression:

$$v = \omega/k' = \omega/(k^2 - m^2/4)^{\frac{1}{2}} = c/(1 - m^2c^2/4\omega^2)^{\frac{1}{2}}$$
$$\dots (4.16)$$

The absorption coefficient, which is represented by α, describes a falling off of amplitude with increasing area of cross-section.

The velocity is seen to be a function of frequency. Thus if a number of different frequencies are propagated simultaneously the group velocity (see Chapter 2, p. 26) must be taken into account.

Equation 4.16 shows that there is a minimum frequency, called the cut-off frequency, below which propagation is not possible. This is given by:

$$\omega = mc/2 \qquad \dots (4.17)$$

The value of the cut-off frequency thus depends on the flare constant m which increases with the amount of spread of the horn. At sufficiently high frequencies the term $m^2c^2/4\omega^2$ becomes negligible compared with unity and the velocity tends to that for plane waves in an unenclosed gas.

Torsion Waves in Rods

It is possible to generate shear waves in a rod so that the vibrations are polarized along the arcs of circles concentric with the axis of the rod. These are called torsion waves. It can be shown (see, for example, Newman and Searle[2], page 108) that the relationship between the couple C causing unit angle of twist over unit length of rod is given by the expression:

$$C = \pi G a^4 / 2$$

where a represents the radius of cross-section and G the rigidity or shear modulus of the material.

Consider a short length δx of the rod in the same way as the thin layer in *Figure 9* and assume that the angle of twist θ varies linearly with distance x along the rod. The couples acting on opposite sides of the layer are respectively $C\partial\theta/\partial x$ and $C\{(\partial\theta/\partial x)+(\partial^2\theta/\partial x^2)\,\delta x\}$. The resultant couple acting is thus $C(\partial^2\theta/\partial x^2)\,\delta x$. From Newton's Second Law this is equal to the product of the moment of inertia of the layer about its axis of rotation and the angular acceleration, viz,

$$(\pi G a^4/2)\,(\partial^2\theta/\partial x^2)\,\delta x = \rho\,(\pi a^2 \delta x)\,(a^2/2)\,\partial^2\theta/\partial t^2$$

i.e.

$$\partial^2\theta/\partial t^2 = (G/\rho)\,\partial^2\theta/\partial x^2 \qquad \ldots (4.18)$$

Thus the velocity of torsion waves in the rod (cf. equation 2.4) is given by the expression:

$$c = (G/\rho)^{\frac{1}{2}} \qquad \ldots (4.19)$$

Flexural Vibrations

Rods and Bars

Thin rods and bars can be set up into transverse vibrations, a well-known example being the oscillations of the reeds of the harmonica. The propagation of the resultant waves is studied with reference to the bending of beams.

It can be shown (see, for example, Newman and Searle[2], page 117) that when a bar is elastically deformed by the application of a force F perpendicular to its neutral axis, the bending moment G arising from the resulting internal elastic forces is given by the expression:

$$G = YSk_r^2 \, d^2y/dx^2 \qquad \ldots (4.20)$$

where the x axis coincides with the neutral axis of the constrained beam, S is the area of cross-section, k_r the radius of gyration of the cross-sectional area about the neutral axis, and Y the Young's modulus. Provided that the weight of the beam is very small compared with F, we have that:

$$F = -\partial G/\partial x$$

Now the forces causing the transverse vibrations of a bar are those responsible for its bending. Consider a thin layer AB of the beam of thickness δx situated with its surfaces perpendicular to the axis (similar to the layer in *Figure 9*) and let F be the force acting at A. The force acting at B will then be equal to $F + (\partial F/\partial x) \, \delta x$. From Newton's Second Law the excess force is equal to the product of the mass and acceleration of the layer, i.e.,

$$(\partial F/\partial x) \, \delta x = (S\rho\delta x) \, \partial^2 y/\partial t^2$$

where ρ is the density of the material of the bar, i.e.,

$$\partial^2 G/\partial x^2 = -S\rho\partial^2 y/\partial t^2$$

But from equation 4.20 we have:

$$\partial^2 G/\partial x^2 = YSk_r^2\rho\partial^4 y/\partial x^4$$

Thus

$$\partial^4 y/\partial x^4 + (\rho/Yk_r^2) \, \partial^2 y/\partial t^2 = 0 \qquad \ldots (4.21)$$

This is the wave equation for transverse waves passing through a rod or bar. Although the waves are transverse they are not shear waves because, to a first degree of approximation, the stresses and strains associated with the vibrations are compressional.

The solution to equation 4.21 for progressive waves can be written as follows:

$$y = A \exp j\omega \, (t - x/v)$$

where v is the wave velocity, the value of which is given by the expression:

$$v = (\omega c k_r)^{\frac{1}{2}} \qquad \qquad \dots (4.22)$$

where $c = (Y/\rho)^{\frac{1}{2}}$ is the longitudinal wave velocity for the rod. It is seen that v is a function of frequency and, where a number of different frequencies are propagated simultaneously, the group velocity v_g must be used (see Chapter 2, p. 26).

For stationary waves in bars vibrating flexurally, one must take into account the boundary conditions, e.g., whether an end is free or clamped. Because of the variation of velocity with frequency the overtones of the fundamental frequency will not be harmonics. For further information on this subject the reader is referred to Sharman[4], page 114.

A well-known example of stationary waves in a transversely vibrating bar is that of the tuning fork. Here the bar is bent and supported at two nodes close together on either side of the centre. The position of the nodes is such that the production of overtones is difficult. In this way a note which is very nearly pure can be obtained.

Plates

Flexural vibrations in plates may be studied from the point of view of the propagation of flexural waves in two dimensions. Stationary wave formation has been investigated by sprinkling the surface with fine sand or some other marking device. The nodal lines are thus rendered visible. The resulting patterns, which are often very attractive to the eye, are called Chladni figures.

The bell is an example of a stationary wave system for modified two-dimensional flexural vibrations. It produces a pure tone in the same way as the tuning fork for a one-dimensional system.

Transverse Waves in Stretched Strings and Membranes

Propagation in a stretched string is caused by disturbing it at some point either by plucking, bowing, or striking it. Because the disturbed portion is displaced laterally the resulting waves are transverse. For a perfectly flexible string the vibrations arise from the tension in it and its inertia; they are independent of the elastic constants of the material.

The velocity of transverse waves in a stretched string is obtained as follows. Let T be the tension and μ the mass per unit length. Suppose that a portion of the string is displaced laterally and let AB (*Figure 22*) represent a small

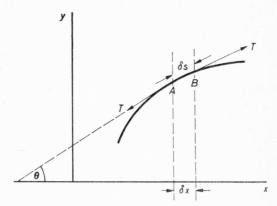

Figure 22. Tension acting in a short length of a stretched string which has been displaced

section of length δs. Let the tangent at A make an angle $\theta = \tan^{-1}(\partial y / \partial x)$ to the x axis. If θ is small, $\theta \simeq \tan \theta = \partial y / \partial x$ and $\delta s \simeq \delta x$. Now the tension acting at A in the y direction to restore the displaced portion to equilibrium equals

$$T \sin \theta \simeq T \partial y / \partial x$$

and that acting at B is

$$T \partial y / \partial x + T (\partial^2 y / \partial x^2) \, \delta x$$

Thus the resultant force producing an acceleration is

$$T \, (\partial^2 y / \partial x^2) \, \delta x$$

so that

$$T \, (\partial y^2 / \partial x^2) \, \delta x = \mu \, (\partial^2 y / \partial t^2) \, \delta x$$

or

$$\partial^2 y / \partial t^2 = (T / \mu) \, \partial^2 y / \partial x^2 \qquad \ldots . (4.23)$$

The velocity v of transverse waves in a stretched string is thus given by the expression:

$$v = (T / \mu)^{\frac{1}{2}} \qquad \ldots . (4.24)$$

A membrane can be considered to be a stretched string extending in two dimensions. Stationary waves in strings and membranes can be regarded in the same way as stationary waves in one or two dimensions in elastic media. A fuller treatment of this subject has been given by Sharman[4], page 94.

Absorption of Sound Waves

In this section a brief account is given of the causes of absorption of sound waves in materials; a more detailed discussion has been provided by the author elsewhere[1].

Absorption in Fluids

The causes of absorption of sound in fluids include viscosity, thermal conduction, and molecular energy exchanges. In general it is found that losses due to these factors become appreciable at ultrasonic frequencies.

Viscous losses arise from the fact, mentioned at the start of this chapter, that a fluid is subjected to shear stresses when compression waves pass through it. A flow of fluid takes place due to the shearing and this depends, in accordance with Newton's law of viscosity (see, for example, Newman and Searle[2], page 219), on the coefficient of viscosity η of the fluid. This flow of fluid is an alternating one having the same frequency as the sound waves. As the wave frequency increases, the viscous motion, being unable to follow the variations of stress, lags in phase behind the wave motion and energy losses occur; the resultant absorption coefficient $\alpha_{vis.}$ is given by the expression:

$$\alpha_{vis.} = (8\pi^2/3)\,(\eta/\rho c^3)\,f^2 \qquad \ldots (4.25)$$

where ρ is the density and c the acoustic velocity for the medium; f is the frequency. For both liquids and gases this quantity becomes significant at frequencies of the order of a megacycle.

Thermal conduction losses may be considered by assuming that the fluid consists of a large number of thin parallel layers perpendicular to the direction of wave motion. Because of the sinusoidal distribution of acoustic pressure with distance, at any given time some of the layers will be compressed and others expanded. The compressed layers are at a higher temperature than the expanded ones and, if it were not for adiabatic conditions holding, there would be a flow of heat. At very high frequencies the regions of high and low temperatures are close together and very high temperature gradients appear, resulting in a departure from the adiabatic state, and a flow of heat takes place. This causes a small overall increase in temperature of the medium and an absorption of sound thus occurs. The corresponding absorption coefficient α_{th} is expressed as follows:

$$\alpha_{th} = (2\pi^2 K/\rho c^3 c_v)\,f^2\,(\gamma-1)/\gamma \qquad \ldots (4.26)$$

where K is the coefficient of thermal conductivity, c_v the specific heat at constant volume, and γ the ratio of the principal specific heats for the medium. For liquids the value of α_{th} is small compared with $\alpha_{vis.}$ but for gases $\alpha_{th} \simeq \frac{1}{2}\alpha_{vis.}$ for a given material.

Losses due to molecular internal energy exchanges in liquids and gases may be caused by thermal relaxation or, in liquids only, by structural relaxation. Thermal relaxation takes place in polyatomic fluids (i.e., those having molecules containing more than one atom each). A proper explanation of this phenomenon is well beyond the scope of this book but it can be said that it arises from exchanges of energy between different internal thermal states of the molecules. Absorption occurs because of phase differences between the alternating exchanges of energy and the acoustic waves; this is a function of frequency. Structural relaxation, which occurs in associated liquids, such as water, the alcohols and glycerol, arises from their lattice structure; the passage of a sound wave may cause a displacement of a molecule from one position in the lattice to another. This displacement will alternate with the same frequency as the sound wave; absorption occurs when it becomes out of phase with the sound waves.

Absorption in Solids

Absorption of sound in solids may be caused by a number of different factors, mainly effective at ultrasonic frequencies, such as the effect of grains in a polycrystalline solid, defects in a crystal lattice, ferromagnetic and ferroelectric effects, interactions between sound waves and electron motion (electron–phonon interactions), and interactions between sound waves and lattice vibrations (phonon–phonon interactions).

Although a polycrystalline solid may be isotropic because of the random orientation of its grains, the grains themselves are usually anisotropic. This leads to differences in characteristic impedances for given directions at grain boundaries; reflection thus occurs and the sound beam will be diffracted or scattered, depending on the grain size and the acoustic frequency (see Chapter 3, p. 48). Rayleigh scattering, for which the attenuation is proportional to the mean grain volume, becomes noticeable at frequencies greater than a megacycle or so. Also, because of the non-uniformity of characteristic impedance, some grains will be compressed or expanded more than others for a given acoustic pressure; a non-uniformity of temperature distribution thus occurs. This gives rise to thermal conduction, and losses due to the overall heating of the material will take place. Absorption may also occur because of the viscous slip along the grain boundaries.

Absorption can take place in crystalline solids because of the presence of dislocations and impurity atoms in the lattice. In ferromagnetic materials losses may occur because the alternating compressions and rarefactions caused by the sound waves will cause the domains to suffer periodic changes in their magnetic states as a result of magnetostriction; this gives rise to magnetic hysteresis losses. Similar phenomena cause absorption in ferroelectric materials (e.g., barium titanate). At low temperatures absorption of ultrasonic waves in single crystal specimens of metals due to the interaction of sound waves with the motion of electrons has been observed. At very high ultrasonic frequencies observations in single crystals of insulating materials and some semiconductors have revealed absorption due to the interaction of sound waves with the lattice vibrations in the materials.

REFERENCES

[1] Blitz, J. *Fundamentals of Ultrasonics.* 1963. London; Butterworths

[2] Newman, F. H. and Searle, V. H. L. *The General Properties of Matter,* 5th ed. 1957. London; Arnold

[3] Wood, A. *Acoustics,* p. 252. 1940. London; Blackie

[4] Sharman, R. V. *Vibrations and Waves.* 1963. London; Butterworths

[5] Kaye, G. W. C. and Laby, T. H. *Tables of Physical and Chemical Constants,* 11th ed. 1957. London; Longmans Green

FURTHER READING

Kinsler, L. E. and Frey, A. R. *Fundamentals of Acoustics.* 1950. New York; Wiley/London; Chapman and Hall

Lindsay, R. B. *Mechanical Radiation.* 1960. New York; McGraw-Hill

Morse, P. M. *Vibration and Sound,* 2nd ed. 1948. New York; McGraw-Hill

Stephens, R. W. B. and Bate, A. E. *Wave Motion and Sound.* 1950. London; Arnold

5

ELECTROMECHANICAL AND ELECTROACOUSTICAL ANALOGIES

Introduction

The mathematics used to solve problems on vibrations and sound waves is often similar to that for the analysis of electrical oscillations; for this reason a.c. electrical theory is commonly used to solve such problems. For example, in Chapter 1 similar differential equations are used for free and forced harmonic vibrations and electrical a.c. circuits, and the idea of a mechanical impedance was introduced by analogy with electrical impedance. In Chapter 2 a further analogy, i.e. of specific acoustic impedance of sound waves in free media with electrical impedance, was described. In this chapter it is shown how the uses of analogies can often enable one to obtain a simple method of solving what could otherwise be a very difficult problem.

Electromechanical Analogies

In Chapter 1, page 11, it is shown that the equation of motion of a helical spring fixed at one end and attached to a mass at the other, when set into periodic motion by the application of an applied sinusoidally varying force F, is similar to a series electrical LCR circuit to which a periodic e.m.f. E is applied (see *Figure 23*). The corresponding electrical and mechanical quantities are listed in Table 5.

One problem is to decide whether the various elements of impedance in the analogous electrical circuit are in series or parallel with one another. This should not prove to be difficult if one realizes that, for electrical circuits, two elements in series pass the same current but share the potential difference, and two elements in parallel have the same potential difference across them but share the current. Thus

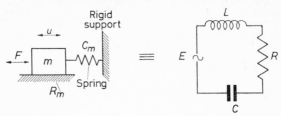

Figure 23. Electrical analogy of forced vibrations of a body of mass m attached at one end to a spring of compliance C_m, clamped at the other end, with frictional resistance R_m

Table 5. Analogous Electrical, Mechanical and Acoustical Quantities

Electrical		Mechanical		Acoustical	
e.m.f.	E	Force	F	Acoustic pressure	p
Charge	q	Displacement	y	Volume displacement	Y
Current	i	Velocity	u	Volume velocity	U_v
Resistance	R	Frictional resistance	R_m	Acoustic resistance	R_A
Capacitance	C	Compliance ($=1/$stiffness)	C_m	Acoustic capacitance	C_A
Inductance	L	Mass	m	Inertance	M

for mechanical vibrations, if two elements have the same velocity (or suffer the same displacement) and, hence, share the applied force, their electrical equivalents are in series; if the elements each suffer the same force and thus share the velocity (or displacement) their electrical equivalents lie in parallel with one another.

Suppose that the spring shown in *Figure 23* is replaced by two parallel springs having compliances C_{m1} and C_{m2}, respectively (see *Figure 24*). It may at first appear that the two compliances should be represented by two capacitances in parallel but it will then be seen that they both suffer the same displacement and thus have the same velocity. Consequently the elements share the applied force and must be represented by series capacitors. The mass m and the frictional

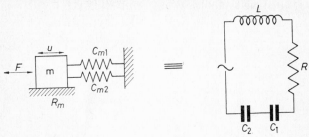

Figure 24. As Figure 23 but with spring replaced by two springs in parallel having compliances C_{m1} and C_{m2}, respectively

resistance R_m are represented by two series components because the friction is experienced over the same distance that m is displaced. Furthermore, because the far ends of C_{m1} and C_{m2} are fixed, m suffers the same displacement as these springs. Thus all the elements are represented by impedances in series.

Consider what happens when an additional mass m' is connected to m by means of a spring of compliance C'_m. Let R'_m be the frictional resistance associated with m' and suppose a force F is applied to m' (see *Figure 25*). Now the displacement of the system m, C_{m1}, and C_{m2} will be equal to the difference between the displacements of m' and C'_m. C'_m is thus represented by a capacitance C' in parallel with the impedances corresponding to that system. This is also seen from the fact that C'_m will transmit the whole of the force F to the system. m' is represented by the inductance L' in series with the combination C', L, C_1, and C_2 because it suffers the same displacement as the system C'_m, M, C_{m1}, and C_{m2}.

The velocities and forces corresponding to the various components of impedance can then be obtained by the use of mesh currents such as i_1 and i_2 corresponding to the velocities u_1 and u_2, respectively, and by applying Kirchhoff's laws (see *Figure 25*). Important applications of this type of analogy include the design of microphones (see Chapter 8, page 104) and problems connected with the isolation of vibrations (see Chapter 6, page 85).

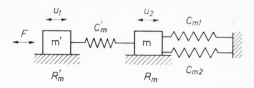

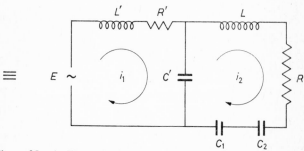

Figure 25. As Figure 24 but with the applied force transferred to another mass m′ connected to m by a spring having a compliance C'_m and with an additional frictional resistance R'_m

Electroacoustical Analogies

Problems concerning the propagation of sound waves in media having finite cross-sections can often be solved very simply by the use of electrical analogies. Here, as also for plane waves in unbounded media, the acoustic pressure p corresponds to voltage but one considers volume velocity $U_v = Su$, S being the area of cross-section, and not the particle velocity u as being equivalent to current. Consequently the volume displacement $Y = Sy$, y being the particle displacement, corresponds to the electric charge.

It is assumed that plane waves are propagated and that the impedance elements have dimensions which are small compared with wave-length. Thus the values of p, U_v, and Y

remain constant at any given time over the whole of the element.

The acoustic impedance Z_A, which should not be confused with the specific acoustic impedance Z_a defined in Chapter 2, page 20, is defined as:

$$Z_A = p/U_v = p/Su \qquad \dots (5.1)$$

This, in general, is a complex quantity which can be expressed as:

$$Z_A = R_A + jX_A$$

where R_A is called the acoustic resistance and X_A the acoustic reactance. As before $j = (-1)^{\frac{1}{2}}$.

The value of R_A for a gas flowing in a tube having uniform area of cross-section can be obtained from Poisseuille's equation (see, for example, Newman and Searle[1]) which is valid for non-turbulent unidirectional flow, i.e. corresponding to d.c., as follows:

$$U_v = \pi a^4 p / 8\eta l$$

where l represents the length of the tube, p the pressure difference between its ends (corresponding to electrical potential difference), a the radius of cross-section, and η the coefficient of viscosity of the gas. Hence we have that:

$$R_A = p/U_v = 8\eta l/\pi a^4 \qquad \dots (5.2)$$

Because the fourth power of the radius is involved in this equation, the term corresponding to electrical resistivity (i.e., $8\eta/a^2$) is a function of the radius of the tube in addition to the viscosity of the fluid; thus no useful purpose can be served by trying to obtain an acoustical analogy with electrical resistivity.

The analogy with electrical inductance is the inertance M of a constriction. This is given by the expression:

$$M = m/S^2 \qquad \dots (5.3)$$

where S represents the area of cross-section of the constriction and m is the mass of the fluid contained within it. The relationship between M and m comes from a consideration of the kinetic energy of the mass of fluid, i.e.,

$$\tfrac{1}{2}mu^2 = \tfrac{1}{2}m \, (Su)^2/S^2 = \tfrac{1}{2}MU_v^2 \qquad \dots (5.4)$$

The corresponding electrical energy of an inductance L carrying a current i is $\tfrac{1}{2}Li^2$.

The acoustic capacitance C_A is defined as the ratio Y/p (cf. C = charge/voltage in electricity) and describes the compliance of an expanding or contracting fluid contained in a cavity of volume V. When an applied pressure p gives rise to a change Y in volume we have that, for an elastic medium:

$$p = KY/V \quad \text{(Hooke's law)}$$

where K represents the bulk modulus. K can be substituted for q in equation 2.8 and will thus be equal to ρc^2. Thus we have that:

$$C_A = Y/p = V/\rho c^2 \qquad \dots (5.5)$$

Acoustic analogies have proved useful for the design of acoustic filters and for the investigation of stationary waves in tubes. To decide whether the electrical equivalents of the elements are in series or parallel one uses the same rules as for mechanical systems (see under Electromechanical Analogies).

Transformer Analogies

The transference of energy from one element to another is most efficient when both elements have impedances of the same order of magnitude, i.e., when the impedances are well matched. This is clearly seen in Chapter 3, page 32, where it is shown that 100 per cent transmission of plane waves takes place across the boundary from one medium to another when both media have the same characteristic impedances. Where the impedances differ from one another by an appreciable amount, only a small proportion of the incident energy is transmitted. The transfer, however, can be made more effective by interposing a layer of a third medium having a suitable thickness and characteristic impedance (see equation 3.14); this layer is an example of an acoustic transformer. Other examples of acoustic transformers are tubes and horns (see pp. 73 and 77). Equations 5.16 to 5.19 (inclusive) and 5.24 show how the terminating impedances of the transformer elements depend on their dimensions and the wave frequency.

An acoustic transformer can be represented by its analogous electrical circuit. In the electrical case the transformer consists of two coils, the primary and secondary. Where the coils are tightly coupled, i.e., the same magnetic flux links both coils, one can relate the e.m.f.'s, E_1 and E_2, the currents i_1 and i_2, and the numbers of turns n_1 and n_2 of the primary and secondary, respectively, by the expression:

$$E_1/E_2 = i_2/i_1 = n_1/n_2$$

The corresponding impedances are then related as follows:

$$Z_2/Z_1 = \frac{E_2}{i_2} \bigg/ \frac{E_1}{i_1} = n_2^2/n_1^2$$

Where it is convenient to represent electric currents and acoustical or mechanical vibrations in a single circuit, the transducer performing the transformation may be represented by a transformer (see *Figure 39b*, page 109). Thus, if F is the mechanical force corresponding to the voltage V across the transducer, we have that:

$$F/V = \alpha_T$$

where α_T is called the transformation factor (see, for example, Blitz[2]). This is analogous to the ratio n_2/n_1 of the number of turns. If Z_e and Z_m are the electrical and mechanical impedances, respectively, it is seen that

$$Z_m/Z_e = \alpha_T^2$$

Acoustic Filters

One well-known type of acoustic filter is the Helmholtz resonator, which consists of a cavity with a narrow neck as its opening. The cavity has a compliance C_A and the fluid contained within the neck has an inertance M. This forms an oscillating system when an external periodically varying pressure is applied to the neck, and the fundamental frequency f_0 for resonance is given by the expression

$$f_0 = 1/2\pi (MC_A)^{\frac{1}{2}} \quad \text{(cf. } f_0 = 1/2\pi (LC)^{\frac{1}{2}} \text{ in the electrical case)}$$
$$\dots . (5.6)$$

Making the substitutions from equations 5.3 and 5.5 we have:

$$f_0 = (c/2\pi)(S/lV)^{\frac{1}{2}} \qquad \ldots (5.6a)$$

where the length l of the neck is related to the mass m of air contained within it by the expression $m = lS\rho$. If some absorbent material is placed inside the resonator a resistance R_A appears and the system will have a finite Q factor equal to $\omega_0 M/R_A$, where $\omega_0 = 2\pi f_0$, in accordance with equation 1.25. Equation 1.26 shows that this will also be equal to $f_0/(f_2 - f_1)$. The difference $f_2 - f_1$ is the frequency bandwidth of the resonator for an intensity drop of 3 dB from the

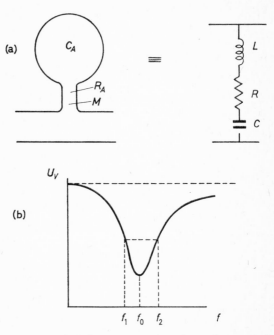

Figure 26. (a) Helmholtz resonator branching off acoustic line to give rise to a narrow band-stop filter, together with the electrical analogy; (b) Frequency response curve for the line

maximum. The placing of a Helmholtz resonator in an acoustic line as shown in *Figure 26* produces a band-stop filter. Where it is desired to increase the frequency bandwidth or to increase the sharpness of the cut-off, a number of these resonators of different sizes and having overlapping bandwidths are arranged in parallel as in *Figure 27*. *Figure 28* shows how a band-pass filter is obtained. With this device only vibrations having frequencies within the limits of the band are transmitted. *Figure 29* illustrates the simplified arrangements for high-pass and low-pass filters.

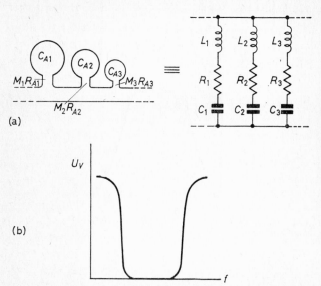

Figure 27. (a) Part of a series of Helmholtz resonator branches off acoustic line to give rise to a broad band-stop filter with a sharp cut-off, together with the electrical analogy; (b) Frequency response curve for the line

Acoustic Impedance in Tubes of Uniform Cross-Section

The general equation for plane waves in a tube of uniform

73

F

cross-section can be written in accordance with equation 2.2d as follows:

$$y = A \exp j (\omega t - kx) + B \exp j (\omega t + kx) \quad \ldots . (5.7)$$

where A and B are constants. The other symbols have been explained earlier. The first term on the right-hand side of equation 5.7 represents waves travelling in the positive

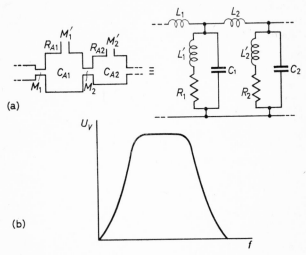

(a)

(b)

Figure 28. (a) Part of acoustic band-pass filter, together with the electrical analogy; (b) Frequency response curve for the line

direction of x, and the second term represents waves of the same frequency moving in the opposite direction. The particle velocity u is then given by the expression:

$$u = \partial y / \partial t = j\omega \left[A \exp j(\omega t - kx) + B \exp j (\omega t + kx) \right]$$
$$\ldots . (5.8)$$

and the acoustic pressure p (see equations 2.5 and 2.8) by the equation:

$$p = - \rho c^2 \partial y / \partial x = jk\rho c^2 \left[A \exp j (\omega t - kx) - B \exp j (\omega t + kx) \right]$$
$$\ldots . (5.9)$$

74

The acoustic impedance Z_A is then expressed as follows:

$$Z_A = p/U_v = p/uS = (\rho c/S) \left[\frac{A \exp(-jkx) - B \exp(jkx)}{A \exp(-jkx) + B \exp(jkx)} \right]$$

$$\ldots . (5.10)$$

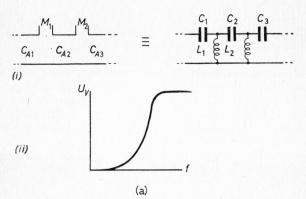

(a)

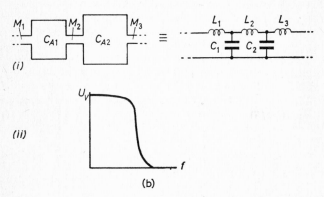

(b)

Figure 29. (a) High-pass and (b) low-pass acoustic filters with electrical analogies (i) and frequency response curves (ii)

75

For purely progressive waves this reduces to:

$$Z_A = \rho c / S \qquad \ldots (5.11)$$

which is entirely real and, hence, represents a pure resistance.

For stationary waves the value of Z_A depends on the boundary conditions at the ends of the tube. If we transform the exponentials of equation 5.10 into their trigonometrical forms we then have:

$$Z_A = \frac{j\rho c}{S} \left[\frac{C \cos kx - \sin kx}{C \sin kx + \cos kx} \right] \qquad \ldots (5.12)$$

where $C = -j(A-B)/(A+B) = \text{constant}$.

Let Z_0 represent the terminating impedance at the end for which $x = 0$. This is given by:

$$Z_0 = (j\rho c / S) C \quad \text{from which} \quad C = Z_0 S / j\rho c$$

Z_A is then expressed in terms of Z_0 as follows:

$$Z_A = \frac{j\rho c}{S} \left[\frac{Z_0 \cos kx + (j\rho c / S) \sin kx}{Z_0 \sin kx + (j\rho c / S) \cos kx} \right] \qquad \ldots (5.13)$$

Let Z_l represent the terminating impedance at the other end for which $x = l$. Thus:

$$Z_0 = \frac{(j\rho c / S) \sin kl + Z_l \cos kl}{\cos kl - Z_l (S / j\rho c) \sin kl} \qquad \ldots (5.14)$$

Z_A can therefore be expressed in terms of Z_l as follows:

$$Z_A = (j\rho c / S) \left[\frac{(j\rho c / S) \sin k(l-x) + Z_l \cos k(l-x)}{(j\rho c / S) \sin k(l+x) + Z_l \cos k(l+x)} \right] \ldots (5.15)$$

Consider a tube containing air closed at one end by a rigid reflecting surface at which there will be a velocity node (see Chapter 3, page 38). Z_l must be infinite because the resultant value of U_v is zero. This gives:

$$Z_0 = -(j\rho c / S) \cot kl \quad \text{(closed end)} \qquad \ldots (5.16)$$

At the open end of the tube there is a pressure node and the terminating impedance Z_l must be zero. Hence:

$$Z_0 = (j\rho c / S) \tan kl \quad \text{(open end)} \qquad \ldots . (5.17)$$

Now where a tube of length l is open at one end and closed at the other (i.e., a closed tube) we have that $Z_0 = 0$ and $Z_l = \infty$. Hence:

$$\cot kl = 0 \text{ and thus } l = (2n - 1) \lambda / 4$$

for which there is quarter wave-length resonance (see Chapter 3, page 41). Where the tube is open at both ends (i.e., an open tube) both Z_0 and Z_l are zero, thus giving:

$$\tan kl = 0 \text{ for which } l = n\lambda / 2$$

for which there is half wave-length resonance (see Chapter 3, page 40).

Where a closed tube is terminated at $x = l$ by a porous material for which the reflection coefficient α_r is less than unity (see Chapter 3, page 38) the value of Z_l is obtained from equations 3.21 and 3.22 as follows:

$$Z_l = P / US = (p_0 / Su_0) (1 + r) / (1 - r) = (\rho c / S) (1 + r) / (1 - r)$$
$$= (\rho c / S) (\text{SWR}) \qquad \ldots . (5.18)$$

where SWR represents the stationary wave ratio (see equation 3.27). Let Z_0 be the acoustic impedance at a distance of one quarter wave-length from the end of the tube, for which $x = \lambda / 4$. From equations 5.14 and 5.18 we have:

$$Z_0 = (\rho c / S)^2 / Z_l = (\rho c / S) (1 - r) / (1 + r) = (\rho c / S) / (\text{SWR})$$
$$\ldots . (5.19)$$

Acoustic Impedance of an Exponential Horn

One can, by analogy with equation 4.15, express the acoustic pressure in an exponential horn by the relationship:

$$p = \exp(-\alpha x) \{A \exp j (\omega t - k'x) + B \exp j (\omega t + k'x)\}$$
$$\ldots . (5.20)$$

where $\alpha = m/2$, $k' = (k^2 - m^2/4)^{\frac{1}{2}}$ and A and B are constants.

This equation takes into account waves travelling in two opposite directions. Now from equation 2.6 we have that:

$$\frac{\partial p}{\partial x} = \rho \frac{\partial u}{\partial t} = -(\alpha + jk') \exp(-\alpha x)\, A \exp j(\omega t - k'x)$$
$$-(\alpha - jk') \exp(-\alpha x)\, B \exp j(\omega t + k'x)$$

from which

$$u = \frac{\alpha + jk'}{j\omega\rho} \exp(-\alpha x)\, A \exp j(\omega t - k'x)$$
$$+ \frac{\alpha - jk'}{j\omega\rho} \exp(-\alpha x)\, B \exp j(\omega t + k'x)$$

and

$$Z_A = \frac{p}{uS} = \frac{j\omega\rho}{S} \left\{ \frac{A \exp(-jk'x) + B \exp(jk'x)}{(\alpha + jk')\, A \exp(-jk'x) + (\alpha - jk')\exp(jk'x)} \right\}$$

$$= \frac{\rho c}{S} \left\{ \frac{A \exp(-jk'x) + B \exp(jk'x)}{[(k'/k) - j(\alpha/k)]\, A \exp(-jk'x)} \right\}$$
$$\qquad\qquad - [(k'/k) + j(\alpha/k)]\, B \exp(jk'x) \right\}$$
$$\ldots\ldots (5.21\text{a})$$

Putting $\sin\theta = \alpha/k$, $\cos\theta = k'/k$, so that $\tan\theta = \alpha/k'$, we have that:

$$(k'/k) - j\alpha/k = \exp(-j\theta) \quad \text{and} \quad (k'/k) + j\alpha/k = \exp(+j\theta)$$

Thus:

$$Z_A = \frac{\rho c}{S} \left\{ \frac{A \exp(-jk'x) + B \exp(jk'x)}{A \exp[-j(k'x + \theta)] - B \exp j(k'x + \theta)} \right\} \ldots\ldots (5.21\text{b})$$

At $x = 0$, $S = S_0$, and $Z_A = Z_0$, and thus:

$$Z_0 = \frac{\rho c}{S_0} \left\{ \frac{A + B}{A \exp(-j\theta) - B \exp(+j\theta)} \right\} \qquad\ldots\ldots (5.22)$$

At $x = l$, $S = S_l$, and $Z = Z_l$, and thus:

$$Z_l = \frac{\rho c}{S_l} \left\{ \frac{A \exp(-jk'l) + B \exp(jk'l)}{A \exp[-j(k'l + \theta)] - B \exp j(k'l + \theta)} \right\} \ldots\ldots (5.23)$$

Eliminating B from equations 5.22 and 5.23 and substituting

ACOUSTIC IMPEDANCE OF AN EXPONENTIAL HORN

trigonometrical functions for the exponentials we have that:

$$Z_0 = \frac{\rho c}{S_0} \left\{ \frac{Z_l \cos (k'l + \theta) + j (\rho c / S_l) \sin k'l}{(\rho c / S_l) \cos (k'l - \theta) + jZ_l \sin k'l} \right\} \qquad \dots (5.24)$$

REFERENCES

[1] Newman, F. H. and Searle, V. H. L. *The General Properties of Matter,* 5th ed., p. 221. 1957. London; Arnold
[2] Blitz, J. *Fundamentals of Ultrasonics,* p. 50. 1963. London; Butterworths

FURTHER READING

Kinsler, L. E. and Frey, A. R. *Fundamentals of Acoustics.* 1950. New York; Wiley/London; Chapman and Hall
Mason, W. P. *Electromechanical Transducers and Wave Filters.* 1948. New York; Van Nostrand
Morse, P. M. *Vibration and Sound,* 2nd ed. 1948. New York; McGraw-Hill
Olson, H. F. and Massa, F. *Dynamical Analogies.* 1943. New York; Van Nostrand

6

HEARING, LOUDNESS, AND NOISE

The Response of the Human Ear

The response of the human ear to sounds of a given frequency but having different intensities varies logarithmically and not linearly. This is in accordance with a more general physiological relationship called the Weber–Fechner law, which states that the stimulus varies in proportion to the logarithm of the stimulant. In acoustics the stimulant is the intensity I and the stimulus is the loudness L, i.e.,

$$L \propto \log I \qquad \qquad \dots (6.1)$$

Because of this logarithmic relationship it is the practice to use the decibel scale (see Chapter 2, page 22) for measuring intensity. It so happens that 1 dB, which represents a change of intensity of about 25 per cent, is the minimum variation detectable by the human ear. Experiments on a large number of persons have shown the existence of (a) the threshold of audibility and (b) the threshold of feeling (or pain). These are frequency dependent (see *Figure 30*); the threshold of audibility represents the lowest intensity level to which the human ear can respond and the threshold of feeling is the highest intensity level which will not produce any discomfort. The lowest intensities for the threshold of audibility occur within the frequency range 1,000 to 3,000 c/s; the threshold intensity level increases considerably on both sides of this range. For frequencies below 20 c/s (infrasonic) and above about 16,000 c/s (ultrasonic) the ear does not respond at all. The upper audible frequency limit usually decreases with the increase in age of the listener; for children the upper limit may be as high as 18,000 c/s.

The threshold pressure describes the r.m.s. value of acoustic pressure at the threshold of audibility for a frequency of

1,000 c/s. This is generally accepted to have a value of 2×10^{-4} dyn cm^{-2} (or microbar). For air, at normal tempera-

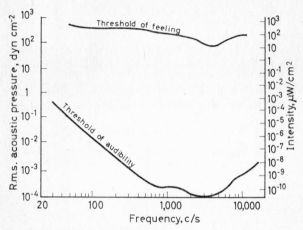

Figure 30. Variations of thresholds of audibility and feeling with frequency

tures, which has a characteristic impedance of 40 c.g.s. units this corresponds to an intensity of 10^{-10} μW cm^{-2} (10^{-9} erg sec^{-1} cm^{-2}) known as the threshold intensity.

Equal Loudness Curves; The Phon

Figure 31 shows what are known as equal loudness curves. These were obtained from experiments conducted on a large number of subjects. Each person tested was placed in a sound-proof room and subjected to a note of given frequency and intensity. As the frequency was changed the intensity was varied by the subject in such a way that the loudness remained at a constant level. Measurements were taken at intervals corresponding to 10 dB at 1,000 c/s from the threshold of audibility to the threshold of feeling. The figure shows that the number of dB between neighbouring curves varied considerably with frequency.

81

Because an increase of 1 dB in intensity produces different increases in loudness at different frequencies another unit has to be defined for the measurement of loudness. This is called the phon; an increase of 1 phon occurs when it is judged equal to an increase of intensity level of 1 dB at 1,000 c/s. At this frequency, and only at this frequency, will the phon and decibel be the same. At the threshold of audibility the loudness is zero phons and at the threshold of feeling the loudness is generally accepted as being 120 phons. Table 6 gives examples of values of loudness for a number of familiar sounds.

Table 6. Loudness Levels for a Number of Familiar Sounds

Sound	Phons	Sones
Threshold of audibility	0	0·065
Quiet whisper	20	0·250
Ordinary conversation	40	1
Inside motor car	50	2
Average office or suburban street with light traffic	60	4
Inside local train	70	8
Noisy office or busy factory	80	16
Busy town street	90	32
Inside tube train	100	64
Near pneumatic drill	110	128
Threshold of feeling	120	256

Hearing Loss and Masking

The curve for the variation of threshold of audibility with frequency (*Figure 30*) will be displaced upwards in places for a person having defective hearing. At a given frequency the number of dB difference between such a person's threshold of audibility and one for a person having normal hearing is called the hearing loss.

When a background noise is present, its intensity will become that of the effective threshold of audibility. For a given frequency the difference in dB between the background noise and the normal threshold of audibility is known as the masking.

The Sone

The phon scale is not altogether satisfactory for noise measurements because a loudness of, say, 80 phons does not appear to be double that of 40 phons. The use of the sone

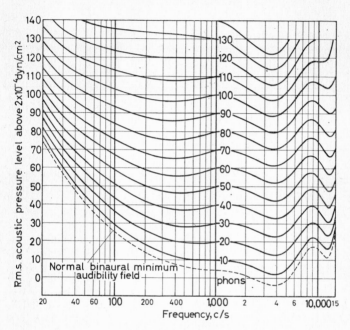

Figure 31. Normal equal loudness contours for pure tones
(binaural free-field listening)
(After B.S. 3383: 1961, by courtesy of British Standards Institution)

provides a more realistic method for measuring loudness levels. It is related to the phon as follows: 1 sone is defined as 40 phons and the number of sones is doubled each time there is an increase in loudness of 10 phons; conversely the number of sones is halved when the loudness is decreased by 10 phons. Thus 2 sones = 50 phons, 4 sones = 60 phons, 500 millisones = 30 phons, etc. Algebraically this can be expressed as follows:

$$10 \log_{10} S = (P - 40) \log_{10} 2$$

i.e.

$$\log_{10} S = 0 \cdot 03 \ (P - 40) \qquad \dots (6.2)$$

where S represents the number of sones and P the corresponding number of phons.

Noise

Noise is defined as any sound which is undesired by the recipient. There are many examples of where one man's noise is another's music but there are many more cases in which there is unanimity as to what constitutes noise. Noise can provide much annoyance to the unintentional listener; it has been shown that a person subjected to it continuously over long periods is liable to experience fatigue and even ill-health, and cases have occurred where losses of aural acuity have been experienced. The problem of noise in industry can be a serious one and even when a worker does not apparently experience discomfort it has been shown that there might well be a decrease in his efficiency.

The degree of noise depends on such factors as its intensity, frequency, and duration. Sounds which can be tolerated for short periods may become annoying when extended over longer periods. Two sources of sound may produce the same intensity which need not be very high; one of these may be quite tolerable or even pleasing whereas the other could be regarded as being noisy. In general, the higher end of the audible frequency spectrum is the chief contributor to noise. Examples of noise sources, which are numerous, include jet aircraft, road traffic, machinery, ventilating systems, typewriters, and office computers.

For the elimination of noise, two types of problem are often considered, one dealing with the isolation of structural vibrations and the other with the elimination of airborne noise. These are dealt with briefly in the following sections.

Isolation of Structural Vibrations

The vibrations transmitted to the floor from such sources

of noise as motors, pumps, and typewriters can be eliminated by mounting them on resilient supports. Conversely, vibrations entering a room from the structure of the building in which it is situated can be eliminated by mounting the floor in a similar manner. One example of a suitable resilient support is a pad of some material such as rubber or glass fibre which acts as a spring in parallel with a damper; this can be represented by the electrical analogy (see Chapter 5) of a capacitor in series with a resistor. *Figure 32* illustrates the arrangement of a mass m supported in this manner on a floor having a mass M; it also shows the corresponding electrical circuit. The figure depicts the case in which it is required to isolate m from the vibrations passing through M. Where it is necessary to isolate M from the vibrations of m then L and l are interchanged in the analogous circuit.

The problem is to choose a support having suitable values of C_m and R_m to give the required degree of isolation for the range of frequencies used. The mesh currents i_1 and i_2 are

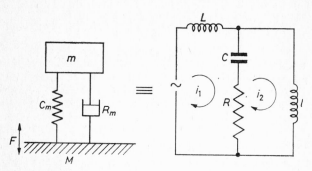

Figure 32. Electrical analogy of a body mounted on a resilient support

proportional to the amplitudes u_1 and u_2 of the vibrations of M and m respectively. Kirchhoff's second law gives:

$$i_2/i_1 = \{R^2 + 1/(\omega C)^2\}^{\frac{1}{2}} / \{R^2 + (\omega l - 1/\omega C)^2\}^{\frac{1}{2}}$$

$$\dots \dots (6.3a)$$

i.e.

$$u_2/u_1 = \{R_m^2 + 1/(\omega C_m)^2\}^{\frac{1}{2}} / \{R_m^2 + (\omega m - 1/\omega C_m)^2\}^{\frac{1}{2}}$$

$$\dots (6.3b)$$

The degree of isolation improves for decreasing values of u_2/u_1; this ratio is seen by inspection of equation 6.3b to be unity at zero frequency, to have a maximum value at the resonant frequency of the system as given by $\omega_0 = 1/(mC_m)^{\frac{1}{2}}$ and then to decrease with increasing frequency. For greatest isolation it is desirable for ω_0 to be as small as possible, for which C_m should have a high value. When ω becomes sufficiently high, the equation reduces to the following:

$$u_2/u_1 = R_m/\omega m \qquad \dots (6.3c)$$

Thus R_m should be small for the degree of isolation to be a maximum.

The characteristics of a resilient support may be obtained by measuring the time period T and the logarithmic decrement δ when the mass m is allowed to vibrate freely. If we combine equation 1.18 (i.e., $\delta = R_m T/2m$) with equation 6.3c we have:

$$u_2/u_1 = 2\delta/\omega T \qquad \dots (6.3d)$$

Thus approximately 60 dB attenuation will occur at a frequency of 25 c/s for a system having a natural frequency of 10 c/s and a logarithmic decrement of 0·008.

Elimination of Airborne Noise

Where the source of noise is in the same enclosure as the listener the intensity may be cut down by reducing the reverberation time (see Chapter 7, page 94). This can be done by having absorbent surfaces on the walls, floor, and ceiling and by the use of soft furnishings.

External airborne noise can be eliminated by constructing the walls, etc., of absorbent material and by the use of such devices as cavity walls and double-glazed windows. It may appear from a consideration of the beginning of Chapter 3 that, except at low frequencies, very little sound would be conducted across a solid wall with air on both sides. This, however, takes into account only longitudinal waves. In practice the walls, panels, etc., can be set up into flexural vibrations. These, however, can be damped if the materials are absorbent.

The trouble of noise from the flexural vibrations of metal panels occurs frequently in the design of passenger vehicles. These vibrations are usually damped by spraying a rubber compound or gluing an absorbent material to the panels.

The Investigation of Noise

Noise is usually investigated by measuring the acoustic intensity at the place required and, if necessary, by carrying out a frequency analysis to ascertain which frequencies are present in the noise spectrum.

For intensity measurements it is desirable to use an instrument having frequency characteristics which are identical with those of the human ear. Such an instrument could measure directly in phons (or sones). The closest approach to this ideal is the sound level meter. This consists of a microphone connected to an amplifier provided with calibrated attenuators, the output of which is fed to a valve voltmeter. The attenuators and the valve voltmeter are graduated in decibels and calibrated with reference to the threshold of audibility at 1,000 c/s. By using a suitable weighting network the instrument can record directly in phons.

Three separate weighting networks, consisting of electrical filters, can be connected to the amplifier. The first, network A, has a frequency response which is similar to the equal loudness curve for 40 phons (*Figure 31*). The response of network B follows the curve for 70 phons and network C provides a flat response over the audible range of frequencies. Thus network A is used for low levels (below 40 phons), network B for medium levels (40 to 70 phons) and network C for high levels (above 70 phons).

Frequency analysis is carried out by using either narrow or wide band analysers. Narrow band analysis comprises the measurement of sound level for a few cycles on either side of a given frequency whereas wide band analysis consists of measurements for bands which will cover either whole octaves or thirds of octaves. Narrow band analysis enables one to obtain a detailed spectrum of the source. This can be useful when it is required to know the various natural frequencies of its vibrations. This method, however, is time consuming and it is often sufficient to obtain simply a third octave or even an octave analysis.

An octave is the interval between two frequencies, one of which is double the other (e.g., 1,000 and 2,000 c/s). A third octave is the interval between two frequencies related by the ratio $2\frac{1}{3}$; for example, the frequencies 1,000, 1,250, 1,600, and 2,000 c/s are approximately at third octave intervals.

It is common practice to record the noise on tape, the recorder having been previously calibrated, and to play it back at one's leisure in the laboratory. The section of tape containing the recorded noise can be cut out and then made into a continuous loop. In this way it can be played back as many times as required through the analysing equipment.

FURTHER READING

Beranek, L. L. *Acoustic Measurements.* 1949. New York; Wiley/London; Chapman and Hall

Beranek, L. L. *Noise Reduction.* 1960. New York; McGraw-Hill

Bruel, Per V. *Sound Insulation and Room Acoustics.* 1951. London; Chapman and Hall

Evans, E. J. and Bazley, E. N. *Sound Absorbing Materials* (National Physical Laboratory). 1960. London; H.M.S.O.

Parkin, P. H. and Humphreys, H. R. *Acoustics, Noise and Buildings.* 1958. London; Faber and Faber

The Use of Sound Level Meters. British Standard BS 1479: 1948

Noise Measurement Techniques (National Physical Laboratory). 1955. London; H.M.S.O.

7

ACOUSTICS OF BUILDINGS

General Considerations

In this chapter we shall discuss the design of buildings from an acoustical point of view. This particular branch of the subject, sometimes called architectural acoustics, concerns the elimination of noise, both internal and external, and methods of obtaining optimum listening conditions, where appropriate. These methods are especially important for theatres, concert halls, school rooms, etc. The chief property of the materials used for the construction of a building and the furnishings placed within it is the absorption coefficient, as defined on page 91. This is important not only for the reduction of noise but also for the choice of a suitable reverberation time, as defined on page 94, to produce the best conditions for listening.

Elimination of Noise

An account of methods of eliminating noise is given in the previous chapter. Structural noise is reduced by such methods as the use of floating floors and airborne noise by using suitable acoustically absorbing materials, examples of which are described under Absorbents. Noise from external sources is reduced by such means as the use of double walls and windows. Ventilation ducts will transmit noise from fans; these can be treated for sound insulation by lining their interiors with suitable materials and by the provision of bends which cause the reduction of sound intensity by multiple reflections.

The Provision of Optimum Listening Conditions

The requirements for optimum listening conditions in auditoria are that all members of the audience can hear the source with sufficient intensity, clearly, and in a pleasing manner. There should be an absence of both echoes and strong resonances, and the reverberation time should be of a suitable length. Too long a reverberation time will produce a lack of clarity and too short a time results in a reduction of intensity and a 'deadness' in the quality of the sound. In general, a shorter reverberation time is required for speech than for music.

The shape of the auditorium should be such that echoes and resonances are reduced, and the materials used for the structure and the furniture should be sufficiently absorbent for this purpose but, on the other hand, should provide a suitable reverberation time. Care should be taken to avoid acoustic 'dead spots' due to selective reflections of waves at certain frequencies, the presence of obstacles, and destructive

Table 7. Values of Absorption Coefficients at Various Frequencies for a Number of Materials*

Material	Absorption coefficient, expressed as a percentage (figures at the head of each column denote frequency in c/s)					
	125	250	500	1,000	2,000	4,000
Rockwool 2·5 cm thick	5·8	19	39	54	59	75
Rockwool 10 cm thick	42	66	73	74	76	79
Glass fibre (loose) 6 cm thick	9·3	39	61	74	83	87
Axminster carpet	11	14	20	33	52	82
Cotton curtain draped to 50 per cent of area	7	31	49	81	66	54
Wood fibre board (ord. soft ¾ in.)	8·5	13	16	30	35	35
Parquet floor on sand foundation	20	15	13	12	9·1	6
Floor boards (ord., varnished) on beams	15	11	10	7	6	7
Glass, large panes	18	6·2	4·1	3	2	1·8
Windows, ord. glass	35	25	18	12	7	4
Distemper on wall	1	1	2	2	3	3
Linoleum ¾ in. thick on concrete	1	1·2	1·5	1·8	2·6	2·6
Rubber flooring on concrete	1·9	3·3	4	3·6	1·8	2

*From Bruel[2], by courtesy of Chapman and Hall.

interference. This can be done by means of suitable reflectors, diffusers, etc.

Absorbents

Absorbents are devices which absorb sound waves; they are characterized by their absorption coefficients. The absorption coefficient α_m is defined here as the ratio of the energy absorbed by the material to the energy incident to it. This should not be confused with the absorption coefficient for a medium, as defined in Chapter 2, page 23. It is a function of both frequency and angle of incidence, and one must thus state whether a particular absorption coefficient refers to a given angle of incidence (usually at right-angles to the surface) or to sound waves integrated for all angles of incidence. Where the sound entering the absorbent is completely absorbed, α_m will be equal to the transmission coefficient α_t as defined in equation 3.13.

Table 7 lists values of absorption coefficients for a number of materials.

Three categories of absorbents can be considered. Firstly there are porous materials such as fabrics, glass fibre, and cotton wool which absorb mainly the higher frequencies. The air in the pores is set up by the sound waves into vibrations which are heavily damped by viscous resistance (see Chapter 5, page 69). Secondly there are membranous absorbents, which consist of airtight materials such as plywood, pulp board, etc., placed at some fixed distance from a solid wall; the space in between may be filled with absorbent material. We thus have a damped oscillating membrane (see Chapter 4, page 61) which will absorb a wide band of frequencies on both sides of the natural frequency of the system. The third type of absorbent consists of cavity resonators which may be either single or multiple Helmholtz resonators (see Chapter 5, page 71). The multiple resonator is frequently found to be mounted on ceilings. It may consist of a board perforated by a large number of holes of equal size arranged in a regular pattern. This is fitted close to and parallel with the ceiling, and the space in between may be filled with some absorbent material. Each hole serves as a neck of a cavity resonator behind which is a portion of the space which acts as the resonating volume.

Absorption of Sound in an Enclosure

Consider a uniform source of sound, having a given frequency, placed in a room and let W represent the value of the power of the source. Sound waves from the source will suffer multiple reflections from the walls, and the intensity at all points within the enclosure will thus increase. For a source having dimensions small compared with wave-length, i.e., virtually a point source, the waves will travel in all directions and, from statistical considerations, it can be shown that, at any time after a short period has been allowed for a sufficient number of reflections to produce a steady state, the intensity will be the same at all points within the enclosure, i.e., the energy density E can be regarded as being constant. This depends on the assumption that there is no interference between the sound waves.

Now the steady state is obtained as a result of the rate of energy lost from the enclosure, due to absorption by the walls, being equal to the rate of supply of energy by the source. It can be shown (see, for example, Kinsler and Frey[1], page 401) that the rate of dissipation of energy in this way is equal to $\frac{1}{4} EcA$, where c represents the velocity of sound in the enclosure and A is defined as follows:

$$A = \alpha_1 S_1 + \alpha_2 S_2 + \alpha_3 S_3 + \ldots = \sum_{m=0}^{m=n} \alpha_m S_m \quad \ldots (7.1)$$

where n is the total number of surfaces bounding the enclosure, for which each has an area S_m and an absorption coefficient α_m (as defined previously, under Absorbents). A is called the total surface absorption or the open window area and will be equal to the equivalent area of open window if the rest of the enclosure surfaces are considered to be 100 per cent reflecting. In addition, absorption will occur in the medium inside the enclosure but where the medium is air at ordinary pressure, in which only audible frequencies are propagated, and where the reflection coefficient is not too great (as found in ordinary rooms), this will have negligible effect compared with absorption by the bounding surfaces.

The diffuse intensity I_D of the sound inside the enclosure is defined as the ratio of the rate of loss of energy $\frac{1}{4} EcA$ to the open window area A, i.e.,

$$I_D = \frac{1}{4} Ec \quad \text{(cf. } I = Ec \text{ for plane progressive waves)}$$

$$\ldots \text{(7.2)}$$

Where the source has a constant power W, it can be seen that when the steady state is reached:

$$W = \frac{1}{4} EcA \quad \text{(steady state)} \qquad \ldots \textbf{(7.3a)}$$

or

$$I_D = W/A \quad \text{(steady state)} \qquad \ldots \text{(7.3b)}$$

Rate of Growth and Rate of Decay of Sound in an Enclosure

In the previous sections the following assumptions had to be made for the statements to be correct: (a) the rate of emission from the source is constant, uniform in all directions, and unaffected by the energy density in the enclosure; (b) no interference of the sound waves occurs; (c) energy is lost only on reflection at the surfaces; (d) the absorption coefficients are not affected by variations of acoustic intensity. It will further be assumed that the energy losses are continuous. This is justified where the surfaces are not too absorbent.

Let V represent the volume of the enclosure. The total energy present at any time time t is then equal to VE and the rate of increase in energy is equal to $\mathrm{d}(VE)/\mathrm{d}t$. Thus:

$$\mathrm{d}(VE)/\mathrm{d}t = W - \frac{1}{4} EcA \qquad \ldots \text{(7.4)}$$

This equation is identical in form with that representing the charging of a capacitance through a resistance and, by analogy, the solution is given by the expression:

$$E = E_0 \left\{ 1 - \exp - (cA/4V)\, t \right\} \qquad \ldots \text{(7.5a)}$$

or

$$I_D = I_0 \left\{ 1 - \exp - (cA/4V)\, t \right\} \qquad \ldots \text{(7.5b)}$$

where E_0 and I_0 represent the steady state values of energy density and diffuse intensity, respectively.

For the decay of intensity in an enclosure, the source is considered to be switched off at a time $t=0$ with the result that W becomes equal to zero in the equation 7.4. The phenomenon is then similar to that of the discharge of a capacitor through a resistor, which leads to the following solution:

$$E = E_0 \exp - (cA/4V)\, t \qquad \ldots (7.6a)$$

or

$$I_D = I_0 \exp - (cA/4V)\, t \qquad \ldots (7.6b)$$

Reverberation Time

The reverberation time for an enclosure is defined as the time taken for a reduction of diffuse intensity of sound inside it by 60 dB after the source has been switched off, i.e., a reduction of intensity to a fraction of 10^{-6} of its original value. This particular value is chosen because it represents a decay from a comfortable listening level to the threshold of audibility. If we substitute the relationship $I_D/I_0 = 10^{-6}$ in equation 7.6b, the reverberation time T can be expressed as:

$$T = mV/A \qquad \ldots (7.7)$$

If the distances are measured in feet, c in air will be 1,100 ft. sec^{-1} and m is equal to 0·05. If, on the other hand, the distances are measured in metres, c in air will be 350 msec^{-1} and m is equal to 0·16. Thus:

$$T = 0·05\, V/A \text{ (distances in feet)} \qquad \ldots (7.7a)$$

and

$$T = 0·16\, V/A \text{ (distances in metres)} \qquad \ldots (7.7b)$$

The equation 7.7 is known as Sabine's formula, which holds for reverberation times of the order of a half-second or more.

Sabine's formula does not hold for reverberation times of less than one half-second. This is because one can no longer assume that the intensity dies down in a continuous manner; the time intervals between each reflection are no longer small compared with the reverberation time. Sabine's formula indicates that T reduces to zero as A becomes infinite. In practice, however, T becomes zero when A becomes equal to the total surface area of the walls of the enclosure. For this value of A, Sabine's formula predicts a finite lower limit to the value of T. A more exact expression for reverberation time, obtained by Eyring, is as follows:

$$T = mV / [-S \log_e (1 - \bar{\alpha})] \qquad \ldots (7.8)$$

where $m = 0.05$ or 0.16, as before, and $\bar{\alpha}$ is the average absorption coefficient for the enclosure surfaces, as defined by:

$$\bar{\alpha} = \sum_{m=1}^{m=n} \alpha_m S_m \bigg/ \sum_{m=1}^{m=n} S_m$$

This expression was derived (see, for example, Kinsler and Frey[1], page 407) from the assumption that the intensity dies down discontinuously. Where $\bar{\alpha}$ is sufficiently small, the expression

$$\log_e (1 - \bar{\alpha}) = -\bar{\alpha} - \bar{\alpha}^2 / 2 - \bar{\alpha}^3 / 3 - \ldots$$

becomes approximately equal to $-\bar{\alpha}$ and Eyring's formula thus becomes identical with Sabine's formula. This happens for values of T of the order of one half-second and more.

Calculations of Reverberation Times

When calculating reverberation times the total open window area A must first be calculated. This is expressed in a unit called the sabin which has the dimensions of square feet. Thus if, at a given frequency, a room has dimensions 20 ft. by 15 ft. by 10 ft., the walls have a mean absorption coefficient of 0.05, the floor is covered with a carpet having an absorption coefficient of 0.25, and the ceiling consists of acoustic tiles having an absorption coefficient of 0.20, the total value of A is 170 sabins. If 10 people are present in the room and we allow 4.5 sabins per person, A becomes 215 sabins. The presence of soft furniture may increase A still further to, say, 240 sabins. Sabine's formula gives 0.6 sec as the reverberation time. Taking a mean absorption coefficient of 28 per cent, Eyring's formula gives practically the same value.

Measurements of Reverberation Times and Absorption Coefficients

For the measurement of the reverberation time in a room a steady source of sound at a given frequency, provided by an oscillator connected to a loudspeaker, is suddenly shut off and the time taken for the diffuse intensity to fall by 60 dB is measured. The intensity is determined by a microphone connected through an amplifier to a valve voltmeter. Best results are obtained when the indications of the valve voltmeter are applied by means of a pen recorder to a calibrated chart moving at a constant known high speed. The recording will indicate the variation of intensity level with time. If a logarithmic amplifier is used the exponential decay will appear as a straight line on the chart and the value of the reverberation time can be obtained from the slope of this line. Thus a decay of as much as 60 dB is not essential. Stationary waves may be avoided by frequency-modulating the source to produce a 'warbling' note.

As an alternative to the steady source of a single frequency one can use a 'white noise' source, i.e., one containing a continuous range of frequencies covering the whole of the audible spectrum, and the required frequency is selected by means of a band-pass filter circuit connected to the microphone amplifier. An ideal white noise source for this purpose is a revolver firing a blank cartridge. This provides a very sudden cut-off of the sound. One can record the report of the revolver on tape and carry out the frequency analysis and reverberation time measurement in the laboratory on a later occasion.

Equation 7.7 shows that reverberation times are functions of the absorption coefficients of the walls of the enclosures. Because these vary with frequency, reverberation times are frequency dependent.

Reverberation time measurements are also used for measurements of absorption coefficients of materials. These measurements are conducted in a reverberation chamber, which is a room having its walls, floor, and ceiling which are almost perfect reflectors. In practice it will have a reverberation time of the order of from 10 to 15 sec or even more. A sample of material having a measured area S is placed on the floor and the reverberation time measured. This gives the open window area $A = \alpha_m S$ from which the absorption coefficient α_m is determined. It may be necessary to make a correction to allow for the effect of the reverberation time of the chamber itself. The value of α_m obtained by this method is the one integrated for all angles of incidence.

If one requires values of absorption coefficient for normal incidence only, the stationary wave method is used, employing the apparatus illustrated in *Figure 33*. The material for

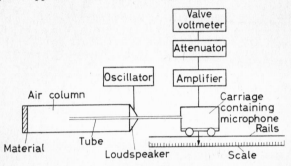

Figure 33. Stationary wave apparatus for the measurements of absorption coefficients of materials

(After Bruel[2].)

which the value of α_m is required is placed at one end of the tube and the loudspeaker, which is perforated at its centre to allow the 'listening tube' to pass through, is excited at a constant level at the required frequency. A stationary wave system is then set up in the tube. The microphone carriage is moved until the maximum reading $V_{max.}$ on the valve voltmeter is obtained; this happens when the mouth of the 'listening tube' is in a position of maximum amplitude (see Chapter 3, page 36). The carriage is then moved until the valve voltmeter reading is a minimum $V_{min.}$, for which the mouth of the 'listening tube' is in a position of minimum amplitude. The ratio $V_{max.}/V_{min.}$ gives the stationary wave ratio SWR as defined by equation 3.27. If it is assumed that no energy is reflected back into the tube from the end of the sample remote from the incident sound waves, the value of the absorption coefficient α_m will be the same as that of the transmission coefficient α_t (see Chapter 3, page 32). Thus:

$$\alpha_m = \alpha_t = 1 - \alpha_r$$

97

But in Chapter 3, page 37, it is shown that $\alpha_r = r^2$. Putting

$$n = \text{SWR} = V_{\text{max.}}/V_{\text{min.}}$$

we have that

$$\alpha_m = 4n/(n+1)^2$$

REFERENCES

[1] Kinsler, L. E. and Frey, A. R. *Fundamentals of Acoustics.* 1950. New York; Wiley/London; Chapman and Hall
[2] Bruel, Per V. *Sound Insulation and Room Acoustics.* 1951. London; Chapman and Hall

FURTHER READING

Consult the list at the end of Chapter 6.

8

THE GENERATION, RECEPTION, AND RECORDING OF SOUND

Acoustic Transducers

A transducer is a device which will enable energy to change from one form to another. Here we are concerned with the conversion of acoustical energy to or from some other form, such as mechanical or electrical energy. For example, most musical instruments are played manually and are thus acousto-mechanical transducers; on the other hand microphones and loudspeakers used for communication purposes are acousto-electrical transducers. Most of these are reversible; examples of these include the moving-coil microphone, which can also be used as a loudspeaker, and the piezoelectric crystal used in ultrasonics.

In this chapter we shall provide a short account of the principal types of microphones, loudspeakers, and ultrasonic transducers. In addition the more important methods of recording and reproducing sound will be mentioned.

Characteristics of Microphones

General Considerations

A microphone will, in general, serve one of two requirements, i.e., (a) for receiving sound waves for communication purposes, e.g., telephony, broadcasting, and recording, and (b) for acoustic measurements. The nature of the requirement will determine the method of the construction and the electro-acoustic characteristics of the instrument. Thus where a microphone is to be used for receiving music it is desirable that its sensitivity should be constant for all frequencies in the audible range. This would not be so important for a microphone used solely for speech telephony and irrelevant where it is used only for measurements at single frequencies, provided that it is known exactly how the sensitivity varies with frequency.

For most applications one would require that a microphone should be highly sensitive, suffer minimum distortion, be

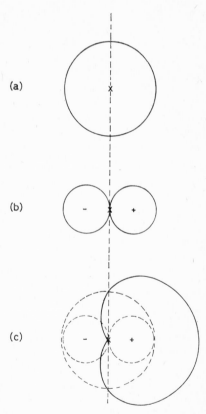

Figure 34. Directional responses of microphones: (a) omnidirectional; (b) 'figure 8'; (c) cardioid [shown to scale as the resultant of (a) and (b)]

100

robust, and provide minimum background noise. In addition, a linear response with frequency may be required. No microphone is ideal in all of these respects and a compromise has to be made in selecting one for a particular application.

Response of a Microphone

The open-circuit sensitivity of a microphone is defined for a given frequency and a given orientation with respect to the direction of the incident waves. It is expressed as the ratio of the potential difference across the terminals, when on open circuit, to the acoustic pressure of the wave at the receiving surface of the microphone. For plane progressive waves the ratio is called the free-field sensitivity. The sensitivity is usually expressed in decibels below 1 volt for an acoustic pressure of 1 dyn cm^{-2}. The variation of the sensitivity with frequency for a microphone is called its frequency response.

It is important to specify direction because there is generally a variation in sensitivity as the diaphragm of the microphone is rotated relative to the direction of the sound waves. This may be caused by such factors as diffraction and cavity resonance. Diffraction can be reduced by ensuring that the dimensions of the microphone are small compared with the wave-lengths used.

In general, the directional properties of a microphone may be classified as follows: (a) omnidirectional, (b) 'figure 8', and (c) cardioid, as shown by the polar diagrams in *Figure 34*. The last is obtained by superposing (a) on (b). An omnidirectional response may be obtained by placing a moving coil microphone in such a position that its diaphragm is horizontal. The figure 8 response occurs for a ribbon microphone for which there is a phase difference of 180 degrees for symmetrical pairs of points on opposite sides of the ribbon. The cardioid response is obtained when a moving coil and ribbon are placed in the same housing. The polar diagrams shown in *Figure 34* hold only where the frequency is sufficiently low for the microphone dimensions to be small compared with the wave-length.

Types of Microphone
The Carbon Microphone

The carbon microphone (see *Figure 35*) has a simple construction, is cheap to buy, has a high sensitivity and a low electrical impedance, is robust, and is reliable in use.

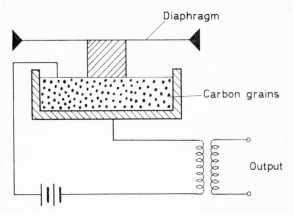

Figure 35. Arrangement of the carbon microphone

The vibrations of the diaphragm, due to the effect of the incident sound waves, cause periodic compressions and expansions of the carbon grains. These result in a periodic variation in the overall resistance of the grains. This gives rise to changes in the direct current through them and thus corresponding changes in the voltage across the terminals of the secondary coil of the transformer.

The carbon microphone suffers the disadvantages of having an irregular frequency response, partly due to the granules tending to pack, and a background hiss being present. It can be seen that the instrument is not a reversible transducer. For its operation both a battery and transformer are required. Because of its unsatisfactory frequency response the carbon microphone is used mainly for purposes for which a high quality of reproduction is unimportant as, for example, the telephone transmitter.

The Condenser Microphone

The condenser microphone is also simple in its design, which consists essentially of two condenser plates; one acts as the diaphragm and is thus movable and the other is fixed (see *Figure 36*). Here again a battery is required; this charges the capacitor, formed by the two plates, through a high resistance. When the diaphragm vibrates as a result of the

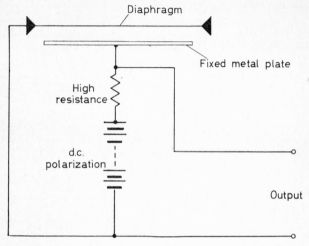

Figure 36. Arrangement of the condenser microphone

sound waves being incident on it, the capacitance changes and there is thus a variation of the charge on the plates and consequently a variation in the current through the resistance. An alternating voltage thus appears across the output terminals. The vibrations of the condenser microphone at audible frequencies are stiffness controlled and, if the resonant frequency is made sufficiently high, the frequency response is flat over the audible range. It possesses the further advantage in that background noises are negligible and it can be made very small in size to avoid diffraction at audio-frequencies. But it is fragile, is easily affected by moisture,

and has a high impedance. A cathode follower is thus necessary to match it to an amplifier. The condenser microphone
can be used for frequencies up to 200 kc/s.

The Moving Coil Microphone

The moving coil microphone is in very common use in both
broadcasting and recording. The diaphragm is attached to a
coil which moves in a magnetic field provided by a permanent
magnet. The rate of change of flux and, hence, the induced
e.m.f. are directly proportional to the velocity of the
diaphragm and thus the acoustic pressure of the incident
waves. In its simplest form, the moving coil microphone is a
damped resonating system with its peak at a frequency at
about 500 c/s. However, by suitable modification the curve
can be considerably flattened to give an almost constant
response over most of the audible range of frequencies. The
usual practice is to use carefully constructed slots and cavities
as in the S.T. & C. 4021 microphone, illustrated together with
the equivalent circuit and response curve in *Figures 37a–d*.
This microphone has a low impedance, is quite sensitive, and
provides practically no background noise.

The Ribbon Microphone

The ribbon microphone consists of a very thin strip of
aluminium foil corrugated in concertina fashion (see *Figure
38*) and held between the poles of a permanent magnet by
means of a pair of terminal clamps at each end. The resonant
frequency of the system is usually only a few cycles per
second, with the result that the vibrations are mass controlled
and the frequency response is very flat. The microphone has
a low impedance, a low background noise, but the sensitivity
is not as high as that of the moving coil microphone.

Crystal Microphones

The element of a crystal microphone is a piezoelectric
crystal (see page 111) for which the voltage across the surfaces
is proportional to the acoustic pressure. It is usual to use
Rochelle salt, which is highly piezoelectric, for audio-
frequencies. The natural frequency of the crystal is well above
the upper frequency limit for audible sound; the response

104

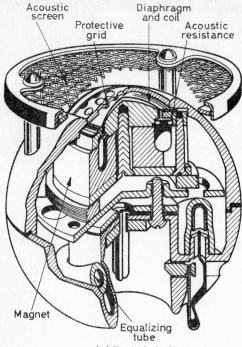

Acoustic screen
Protective grid
Diaphragm and coil
Acoustic resistance
Magnet
Equalizing tube

(a) Exploded view

Figure 37a. The S.T. & C. 4021 moving coil microphone
(From Gayford[2], by courtesy of MacDonald and Evans.
and Standard Telephones and Cables Ltd.)

can thus be made linear, the vibrations being stiffness controlled. Piezoelectric crystals have high electrical impedances
and low sensitivities as microphones. They can, however, be
made so small that the conditions for their dimensions being
of negligible size compared with wave-length applies to all
audible frequencies, i.e., almost non-directional polar diagrams
(see *Figure 34a*) are possible for the whole audio-frequency
range.

Higher sensitivities can be obtained by using a bimorph

105

H

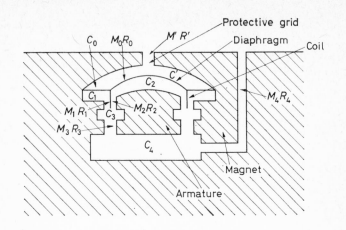

(b) Functional diagram

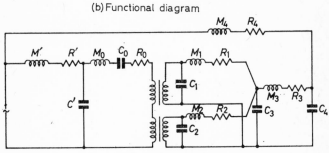

(c) Equivalent circuit

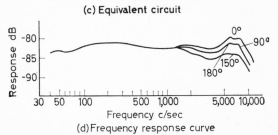

(d) Frequency response curve

Figure 37b–d. The S.T. & C. 4021 moving coil microphone

(From Gayford², by courtesy of MacDonald and Evans, and Standard Telephones and Cables Ltd.)

transducer consisting of two Rochelle salt crystals glued together with their axes orientated in such a way that a contraction of one along a given direction is accompanied

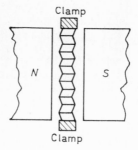

Figure 38. Arrangement of the ribbon microphone

by an expansion of the other along that direction. In this way the system vibrates flexurally with much greater amplitude than for the corresponding compressional vibrations.

Loudspeakers
General Considerations

Although, as shown in the previous section, a number of different types of transducer are used as microphones, most of those used as loudspeakers are electromagnetic in operation, although electrostatic loudspeakers are used to a limited extent. The electromagnetic transducer, if properly designed, can fulfil all the principal requirements of an efficient loudspeaker, namely a high transfer efficiency, faithful reproduction, an output response independent of frequency, and non-directional characteristics over a wide range of frequencies. It is usual to use only the moving coil transducer for the two types of loudspeaker most commonly employed, i.e., the direct radiation and horn speakers. For earphones, however, both moving coil and moving iron types are used. The moving iron transducer is often used as a telephone earpiece, for which a uniform response with frequency is not an important consideration. This consists essentially of a soft iron armature in a magnetic field and attached to a diaphragm. The motion of the armature and, hence, of the diaphragm is controlled by the amplitude and frequency of the magnetic field, which depends on the exciting current.

The Direct Radiation Loudspeaker

With the exception of open-air public address systems, the direct radiation type of loudspeaker is used for practically all purposes for which a loudspeaker is required. Ideally this should have the characteristics of a piston vibrating in an infinite baffle (see Chapter 3, page 44). For this reason it is always mounted in a large baffle or a cabinet. To increase the area of the radiating surface, in order to obtain a higher output, a cone made of paper or some similar light-weight material is attached to the diaphragm. *Figure 39* illustrates the construction of a direct radiation loudspeaker, mounted in a cabinet, and its equivalent electrical circuit. The vibrations radiated backwards into the cabinet suffer a phase change of 180 degrees. This is indicated by the coupling of the impedance Z_c of the cabinet with the moving system by a 1:1 transformer with the windings of the two coils in opposite directions.

At low frequencies the vibrating system may be regarded as having a mass equal to the sum of those of the coil and cone and a compliance which is the resultant of those of the supports of the coil and cone. At high frequencies the cone vibrates in separate zones, each having its share of the mass and compliance. If the cone is constructed of circular corrugations, as shown in *Figure 39a*, the piston-like properties of the vibrations are retained at higher frequencies. For a linear frequency response, attention must be paid to the design of the cabinet as well as that of the transducer itself. The natural resonances of the cabinet must be damped down by such methods as lining the inside with an absorbent material.

A well-designed loudspeaker has a linear frequency response up to about 10,000 c/s. To retain the linear response at higher frequencies it is common to use an additional loudspeaker, called a 'tweeter', which is designed to respond at high frequencies only. This can be either a small horn loudspeaker

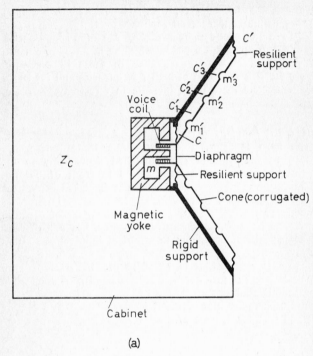

(a)

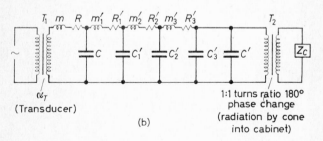

1:1 turns ratio 180°
phase change
(radiation by cone
into cabinet)

(b)

*Figure 39. Direct radiation loudspeaker: (a) arrangement showing
corrugated cone; (b) equivalent circuit*

or an electrostatic speaker, which is designed in a similar manner to the condenser microphone.

Because a well-designed direct radiation loudspeaker resembles in operation a piston vibrating in an infinite baffle, its directivity patterns are similar to those illustrated in *Figure 18*. It is seen that at higher frequencies and for larger cone diameters there is an increase in directivity.

The Horn Loudspeaker

The horn loudspeaker consists of a transducer, nearly always of moving coil type, matched acoustically to the medium by means of a horn placed in front of but not touching the diaphragm. A constriction is placed behind the throat of the horn to prevent any destructive interference of the waves at the throat. The main advantage of the horn speaker is its very high transfer efficiency, i.e., a high ratio of acoustical output energy to electrical input energy. It is, however, highly directional and, where a non-directional response is required, it is usual to use batteries of horn speakers pointing in different directions. Its main application is to public address systems out of doors. An account of the acoustic characteristics of horns is given in Chapter 4, page 54, and Chapter 5, page 77.

Voltage Response of a Loudspeaker

The transfer efficiency of a loudspeaker is often expressed in terms of its voltage response (VR) as given by the expression:

$$VR = 20 \log_{10} (p/p_0)/(E/E_0) \text{ dB} \qquad \ldots \text{(8.1)}$$

where p represents the r.m.s. acoustic pressure produced, and the r.m.s. potential difference is represented by E. p_0 and E_0 are reference pressure and voltage. Where $p_0 = 2 \times 10^{-4}$ dyn cm^{-2} and $E_0 = 1$ V:

$$VR = 20 \log_{10} (p/E) + 74 \text{ dB re } 2 \times 10^{-4} \text{ dyn cm}^{-2} \text{ and } 1 \text{ V}$$
$$\ldots \text{(8.1a)}$$

Ultrasonic Transducers

For most types of transducer used at audio-frequencies, the response diminishes too greatly to be of much use at frequencies in the ultrasonic range (i.e., above 18 kc/s). The most suitable types of transducer for use at ultrasonic frequencies are the piezoelectric, magnetostrictive, and purely mechanical oscillators. A fuller description of these has been given elsewhere[1], and in this section a brief account of their construction and properties is given.

Piezoelectric Oscillators

Piezoelectric oscillators are made of materials which display the piezoelectric effect. If a stress is applied to a slab of such a material in a given direction, equal and opposite electric charges, the magnitudes of which are directly proportional to the applied stress, appear on the surfaces. On the other hand, if a voltage is applied across the surfaces, the plate will suffer a mechanical strain corresponding to the stress and directly proportional to the applied voltage. These are, respectively, the direct ,and converse piezoelectric effects, which are equal and opposite. If the surfaces of the slab are plated with a conducting material so as to form electrodes to which an alternating voltage of a given frequency is applied, the slab will vibrate at that frequency. Conversely, if the plate is placed in an acoustic field and thus vibrates, an alternating potential difference having the same frequency as the sound waves appears across the electrodes. Maximum amplitude of the vibrations and, hence, maximum voltage occur when the applied frequency is equal to a natural frequency of the piezoelectric oscillator.

Quartz crystals display the piezoelectric effect along certain directions called axes of non-symmetry. If a plate is cut from a quartz crystal with its radiating surfaces perpendicular to one of these directions, called the X axis, the vibrations are compressional and compression waves are generated. If, on the other hand, the plate is cut with its radiating surface perpendicular to another of these directions, called the Y axis, the surface vibrates in a tangential direction and shear waves are propagated.

111

The piezoelectric effect is not very strong in quartz, and transducers made from this material are used mainly for the low power applications described in the next chapter. The effect is much more pronounced in transducers made from ceramic materials such as barium titanate, lead zirconate, and lead meta-niobate, and very high powers are possible from such transducers.

When used as microphones, in the audio-frequency range, piezoelectric crystals are operated at frequencies below their fundamental resonances. At ultrasonic frequencies they are almost always operated under conditions of resonance. As a rough guide it can be assumed that, for compression waves, a thickness of 1 cm corresponds to a fundamental resonant frequency of about 250 kc/s; the frequency varies inversely with the increase in thickness. Thus a rectangular plate used to propagate waves at a frequency of 1 Mc/s has a thickness of about 2 mm for its fundamental resonance.

Magnetostrictive Oscillators

The magnetostrictive effect is found with ferromagnetic materials and certain non-metals called ferrites. The direct (or Joule) effect is observed when a rod of such a material is placed in a magnetic field orientated parallel with its axis; a change in length occurs, this being either an increase or a decrease depending on the nature of the material and its physical state. If, on the other hand, a magnetized rod of such a material is subjected to a compressional or tensile stress, a change in the magnetic flux in the rod is observed; this is the converse (or Villari) effect. Provided that the rod is kept polarized by the application of a steady direct magnetic field, the change in length varies approximately linearly with the applied field provided that the strength of the latter does not exceed the strength of the polarizing field. Nickel, which is strongly magnetostrictive, is the material most commonly used as a magnetostrictive transducer.

For the generation of ultrasonic waves, the rod is placed in two coils, one of which carries a direct current to provide the polarizing field and the other of which carries an alternating current to provide the variable magnetic field, the frequency of which being equal to the frequency of the mechanical oscillations of the rod. As before, maximum amplitude occurs when the length of the rod is equal to that for which resonance occurs. *Figure 40* shows a simple

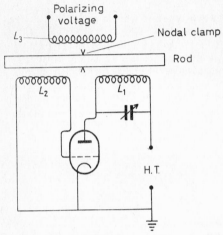

Figure 40. Pierce-type circuit for exciting a magnetostrictive oscillator

arrangement, due to Pierce, in which the rod is clamped at the node in the centre. Coil L_1, the exciting coil, together with the capacitance C in the anode circuit of the triode, form a resonating circuit which can be tuned to the fundamental frequency of the rod. Coil L_2 provides feedback to the grid of the triode so as to maintain the oscillations in the tuned circuit and hence of the rod, and coil L_3 passes the direct current for the polarizing field.

High amplitudes of vibration are possible with magneto-strictive generators at frequencies of up to about 25 kc/s with the result that they are commonly used for high power ultrasonic applications. The power output decreases with increase of frequency at a fairly rapid rate above this frequency limit; this accompanies a decrease in the length of rod, for resonance, with increase in frequency. For nickel, a rod 12·5 cm long has a fundamental resonant frequency of about 20 kc/s.

Mechanical Oscillators

Mechanical ultrasonic oscillators include whistles and sirens. The two types of whistle generally used are the cavity and wedge resonators. The first ultrasonic whistle, designed by Galton in 1900, had a limited range of applications; the best known one was its use as a dog whistle. Improvements in its design have brought forth instruments capable of developing very high acoustic outputs of the order of 50 W at frequencies of about 20 kc/s. In its modern form, due primarily to Hartmann, a jet of gas or liquid is forced through a nozzle at a high velocity and is incident on a cavity or nodally supported wedge in the same fluid (see *Figures 41a*

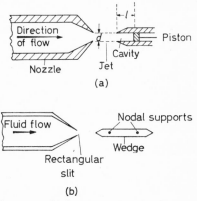

(a)

(b)

Figure 41. Ultrasonic whistles: (a) cavity whistle; (b) wedge whistle

and *b*). Shock waves are produced in the jet and these set the cavity or wedge into vibrations at the natural frequency, the value of which is dependent on the dimensions of the cavity or wedge.

Sirens are also used to generate ultrasonics and they have proved to be effective in generating high outputs at frequencies up to about 25 kc/s. In its simplest form the siren consists of a disc (the rotor) in which are drilled a number of similar holes, spaced equally around the circumference of a circle concentric with it. This is rotated in front of a similar disc (the stator) which is at rest, while jets of fluid are directed through the holes. These jets are interrupted by the motion of the perforations in the rotor relative to those in the stator and intermittent puffs of fluid are released, with the result that sound waves are propagated. The frequency of these waves is given by the product of the number of holes in the disc and the number of revolutions per unit time of the rotor.

The Recording and Reproduction of Sound
General Considerations

Sound is recorded by reproducing the vibrations of the source by a transducer which then produces a trace on a body moving at constant known speed; this body can be a rotating disc or cylinder, or a moving ribbon. The trace is then stored until it is required to reproduce the sound. For commercial purposes it is usually the practice to obtain large numbers of copies of the trace or record in some permanent form. To reproduce the original sound, the record is again set into motion, usually at the speed of recording, and made to actuate a transducer so as to produce a sound identical, as near as possible, with the original.

At the time of writing three methods of recording sound are practised, these being mechanical, optical, and magnetic; in the following sub-sections a brief account is given of these methods.

Much progress is being made in the perfection of stereophonic recording and reproduction to provide a realistic binaural effect. For recording, two microphones are placed in suitable positions and two simultaneous traces are obtained. Two loudspeakers are therefore necessary for faithful reproduction; these must be correctly positioned in relation to each of the listener's ears. The listener should thus not only obtain accuracy in hearing intensity and frequency variations of the source as a whole, but be able to sense these variations in different positions of the source, e.g., to be able to locate the individual instruments in an orchestra. Care must be taken in the design of a stereophonic recording that there is no interference between the two channels.

Mechanical Methods

Mechanical methods of recording and reproducing sound date back to 1876 when Edison patented the phonograph, and this device, now called the gramophone or 'record-player', is the one most widely used. The recording transducer has a stylus attached to it and this stylus cuts a more or less spiral groove in a disc rotating at some constant speed. The exact shape of the groove is determined by the lateral motions of the stylus which are caused by the vibrations of the transducer. Reproduction is obtained by the reverse process in which a stylus (or needle) attached to the transducer (usually called 'pick-up') is set in motion when guided by the grooves whilst the disc rotates at the speed of recording. The motion of the stylus sets the transducer into vibration and the original sound is reheard.

Originally both recording and reproduction were carried out entirely mechanically. In each case the stylus was attached to a vibrating diaphragm and acoustic matching was obtained by means of a horn. Since the 1920s, with the development of electronic amplifiers, electromechanical transducers have been used. The most important advances in this field have been the development of long-play recording and of stereophony. For long-play records the speed of the disc was reduced from the old 78 r.p.m. to $33\frac{1}{3}$ or 45 r.p.m. This was accompanied at the same time by a considerable increase in standard of reproduction. At the time of writing, stereophonic recording by disc is carried out by using a single groove for both channels. The groove has an apex of 90 degrees and its sides are inclined at an angle of 45 degrees to the plane of the disc. The vibrations of the stylus are resolved in two directions at right-angles to each other and each component fed to separate transducers.

Optical Methods

Optical methods of recording are used mainly for sound-tracks of cinematograph films. To obtain synchronization of sound and action, the recording is usually made on the same film as the picture. The two main types of recording are the variable width and the variable density. For the variable width method one obtains a strip of clear film with its boundaries having the same shape as the waveform of the source. For the variable density method the strip is no longer clear but has constant width and its optical density varies in the same way as the acoustic waveform. In both cases a beam of light passes through the sound-track.

For recording by the variable width method the transducer causes a variation of the width of the aperture of the incident beam of light. For the variable density method the transducer causes a variation in the intensity of the beam. Reproduction of either type of recording is carried out by the same method; the beam, after passing through the sound-track, falls on a photo-cell which produces a current varying in the same way as the acoustic waveform.

Magnetic Methods

For magnetic recording and reproduction the acoustic record is stored on a tape covered with a layer of ferromagnetic material. The tape is unwound from a spool, passed at a fixed speed through a small air gap in a magnetic circuit, magnetized permanently, and then wound on to another spool. The recording transducer gives rise to a variation of magnetic flux in the gap, corresponding to the variation in acoustic pressure of the source. The variation of magnetic intensity along the length of the tape reproduces the waveform of the source. The tape is replayed by passing it at the same speed at which it was recorded through an air gap in a transducer similar to the one used for recording. Provision may be made for two or four channels on a single tape. This can allow for a longer replay time or for stereophonic recording. An important advantage of the magnetic tape over other types of recording is that a recording can be erased and the same tape used many times.

REFERENCES

[1] Blitz, J. *Fundamentals of Ultrasonics.* 1963. London; Butterworths

[2] Gayford, M. L. *Acoustic Techniques and Transducers.* 1961. London; MacDonald and Evans

FURTHER READING

Beranek, L. L. *Acoustic Measurements.* 1949. New York; Wiley/London; Chapman and Hall

Briggs, G. A. *Loudspeakers,* 5th ed. 1958. Bradford; Wharfedale

Crawford, A. E. *Ultrasonic Engineering.* 1955. London; Butterworths

Greenlees, A. E. *The Amplification and Distribution of Sound.* 1954. London; Chapman and Hall

Hueter, T. F. and Bolt, R. H. *Sonics.* 1955. New York; Wiley/London; Chapman and Hall

Jones, E. H. *Audio-Frequency Engineering.* 1961. London; Chatto and Windus

Kinsler, L. E. and Frey, A. R. *Fundamentals of Acoustics.* 1950. New York; Wiley/London; Chapman and Hall

Mason, W. P. *Electromagnetic Transducers and Wave Filters.* 1948. New York; Van Nostrand

Mason, W. P. *Piezoelectric Crystals and their Applications to Ultrasonics.* 1949. New York; Van Nostrand

Microphones (B.B.C. Training Manual). 1951. London; Iliffe

9

FUNDAMENTAL ACOUSTIC MEASUREMENTS

Intensity Measurements

For the measurement of intensity at a given point one uses a microphone which has been calibrated under certain specified conditions. This can be done by either comparing it with an 'absolute' receiver subjected to the same intensity, direct actuation by an 'absolute' source, or the method of reciprocity. Either 'free-field' or 'closed chamber' conditions are specified.

For a free-field calibration the measurements are conducted in purely progressive waves of a given frequency from a loudspeaker source. It is essential that the waves are not disturbed by unwanted reflections or external noise. These conditions are satisfied in the open air far from buildings and noise sources; they are also satisfied in a well-designed sound-proof anechoic chamber. This is a room which is completely isolated from external sources of sound and which has boundaries made of a highly absorbent material, such as glass fibre. The anechoic properties of the walls, etc., are improved by the use of absorbent wedges arranged with their thin edges facing the incident waves. In this way the incident waves are almost completely absorbed by multiple reflections (see *Figure 42*). For a perfect free-field, inverse square law conditions should hold for a small source or, in the far zone, for a piston source in an infinite baffle.

For closed chamber measurements the calibration is carried out in a small sound-proof box having its dimensions small compared with wave-length. In this way the acoustic intensity, particle velocity, particle displacement, and acoustic pressure are constant throughout. The closed chamber method is used

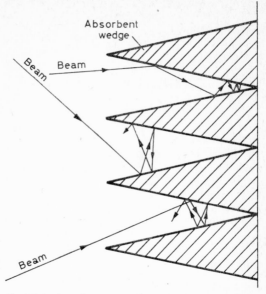

Figure 42. Multiple reflections at the surfaces of absorbent wedges in an anechoic chamber

for reciprocity and actuation calibrations; for reciprocity calibrations it is limited in frequency, e.g., up to 4 kc/s for a chamber volume of a few cubic centimetres.

The open circuit potential difference across the terminals of the microphone is normally measured by connecting it via a transformer or cathode follower, if necessary, to an amplifier fitted with a set of calibrated attenuators; the output is then fed to a valve voltmeter. The potential difference can then be measured directly as the number of decibels below 1 V (see Chapter 8, page 101).

Calibration of Microphones
Calibration by Direct Actuation by a Primary Source

By using a primary source, the output of which can be

determined absolutely, a known alternating pressure may be applied to the diaphragm of the microphone and the sensitivity thus determined directly. At one time the piston-phone and thermophone (see Beranek[1]) were used for this purpose but, at the time of writing, the electrostatic actuator is preferred. This can be used for the closed chamber technique at frequencies too high for accurate reciprocity measurements.

The electrostatic actuator consists simply of a slotted metal plate placed very close to the metal diaphragm of the microphone under test. A polarizing potential difference of about 500 V d.c. is applied across the plate and diaphragm. A known alternating e.m.f. of the order of 20 to 50 V at the required frequency is then applied. It can be shown that the acoustic pressure p is related to the applied voltage E by the expression:

$$p = 8 \cdot 84 \times 10^{-7} \, E_0 E / d^2 \text{ dyn cm}^{-2} \qquad \dots (9.1)$$

where d is the separation distance between the plate and diaphragm in centimetres and E_0 the polarizing voltage, provided that E is much less than E_0.

Calibration by Comparison

To calibrate a microphone by comparison one first places a standard detector at a given point in a sound field, and the acoustic intensity (or acoustic pressure, etc.) is determined for the particular frequency. The standard is then replaced by the test microphone, without altering the properties of the sound waves, and the open circuit voltage across the terminals measured. The sensitivity of the microphone at that frequency (as defined in Chapter 8, page 101) is thus determined. The standard can be either a microphone already calibrated or an absolute detector such as the Rayleigh disc, radiometer, hot-wire microphone, or suspended particles in the medium. A brief account of these absolute detectors is given in the following sub-sections.

The Rayleigh Disc

The Rayleigh disc is used to measure particle velocity amplitude; it consists of a thin circular disc of a light-weight

J

material with reflecting surfaces (e.g., a microscope cover slip). This is suspended by a torsion fibre in the sound field so that its surfaces are parallel with the direction of propagation. The effect of the sound waves is to cause the disc to rotate by some angle θ to a position of equilibrium. This angle is measured by the rotation of a beam of light reflected from the surface (i.e., the optical lever). To a first approximation the torque C acting on the suspension is given by the expression:

$$C = (4/3)\, \rho a^2 u^2_{\text{r.m.s.}} \sin 2\theta \qquad \ldots (9.2)$$

where a represents the radius of the disc, ρ the density of the air, and $u_{\text{r.m.s.}}$ the root mean square of the particle velocity. a should be small compared with wave-length.

The Radiometer

A simple form of radiometer consists of a solid sphere, having its radius small compared with wave-length, suspended vertically. The effect of the sound field is to exert a pressure of radiation (see Chapter 2, page 22) and thus cause a horizontal displacement of the sphere. The angle of displacement of the suspension is related directly to the pressure of radiation and hence to the intensity. The device is calibrated by subjecting the sphere to known static air pressures and noting the corresponding displacements.

The Hot-Wire Microphone

The hot-wire microphone consists of a short length of fine platinum wire, suitably supported and heated to just below redness by the passage of an electric current through it. When it is placed in a fluid stream, either direct or alternating, the wire is cooled by convection and thus suffers a steady drop on resistance. This is directly proportional to the particle velocity amplitude u_0. The microphone is calibrated by placing it in a direct stream of air flowing at a known velocity.

Motion of Suspended Particles

Very light suspended particles, such as cigarette smoke, in a sound field will follow the motion of vibration of the particles of air. If these are observed through a low power microscope a direct measurement of the particle displacement amplitude y_0 is obtained. At higher frequencies in the audible range the inertia of the smoke particles may prevent their amplitudes equalling the amplitudes of the particles of the medium and a small correction may be necessary.

Calibration by the Reciprocity Technique

The reciprocity method of calibration is based on the theory of reciprocity which is best understood by considering two coupled electrical circuits A and B. Let i_A the current in A correspond to an e.m.f. E_A in the same circuit and let it produce an e.m.f. E_B in B. Now the same e.m.f. E_B can also be produced by a current i_B in B. According to the theory of reciprocity, the current i_B in B will produce the e.m.f. E_A in A.

The calibration can be carried out using either the free-field or the closed chamber methods. In both cases a reversible transducer, i.e., one which can act both as microphone or loudspeaker, is required.

Free-Field Reciprocity Calibration

From equation 2.33 it can be seen that the r.m.s. acoustic pressure p at some distance r in a free-field from a small spherical source is given by the expression:

$$p = \rho f U_v / 2r \qquad \qquad \text{.... (9.3)}$$

where ρ and c represent the density and acoustic velocity, respectively, for the medium, usually air; f the frequency, and U_v the r.m.s volume velocity at the source. A transducer having a radius small compared with wave-length behaves, to a high degree of approximation, as a spherical source.

Consider two points A and B distance r apart and let a small reversible transducer be placed at A. A current i through the transducer will give rise to a volume velocity U_v at the diaphragm and a corresponding acoustic pressure p at B in accordance with equation 9.3. Let the transducer then be used as a microphone and a simple source, having the same volume velocity U_v at its surface and the same frequency, be placed at B so that the same pressure p appears

123

at A. Let E represent the corresponding open circuit potential difference across the terminals of the microphone. The theory of reciprocity predicts that since i gives rise to p and U_v gives rise to E under the same conditions:

$$i/p = U_v/E \qquad \dots (9.4)$$

Let $M = E/p$ be the sensitivity of the transducer when used as a microphone and $S = p/i$ define the sensitivity of the transducer when used as a loudspeaker, the quantities being measured in absolute units. Substituting these equalities in equation 9.4 we have that:

$$M = U_v S/p$$

and combining this with equation 9.3 we have that:

$$M = 2rS/\rho f \qquad \dots (9.5)$$

In general, three transducers are required for a reciprocity type calibration, these being T_1, the microphone under test which need not be reversible, T_2 a small reversible transducer, and a loudspeaker T_3. T_1 and T_2 are first placed in position (1) (see *Figure 43*) with a small r.m.s. current i passing

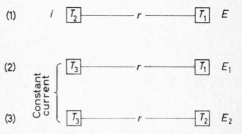

Figure 43. Arrangement of transducers for a free-field reciprocity calibration

through T_2 which acts as a source. E is the resultant open-circuit potential difference across T_1. If p is the acoustic pressure at T_1 we have that:

$$M_1 = E/p \qquad \dots (9.6)$$

124

where M_1 represents the sensitivity of the microphone T_1 under test, and

$$S_2 = p/i \qquad \dots (9.7)$$

where S_2 is the sensitivity of T_2 when used as a loudspeaker. Applying equation 9.5 to T_2, it is seen that:

$$M_2 = 2rS_2/\rho f = 2rp/\rho fi \qquad \dots (9.8)$$

and eliminating p from equations 9.6 and 9.8 we have

$$M_1 M_2 = (E/i) \cdot (2r/\rho f) \qquad \dots (9.9)$$

T_1 and T_2, used as a microphone, are then in turn placed at the same distance in front of the source T_3 with the current through the latter remaining constant [positions (2) and (3) in *Figure 43*]. Let E_1 and E_2 be the corresponding open-circuit voltages across the terminals of T_1 and T_2. We thus have that:

$$M_1/M_2 = E_1/E_2 \qquad \dots (9.10)$$

Thus

$$M_1 = \{(E/i)\,(E_1/E_2)\,(2r/\rho f)\}^{\frac{1}{2}} \text{ V per newton m}^{-2} \qquad \dots (9.11)$$

where each of the quantities is measured in M-K-S. units. Where the distances are measured in cm, the density in gm cm^{-3}, the potential differences in volts (as before) and the current in amps (as before), we have that:

$$M_1 = \{(E/i)\,(E_1/E_2)\,(2r/\rho f) \times 10^{-7}\}^{\frac{1}{2}} \text{ V per dyn cm}^{-2} \qquad \dots (9.12)$$

It is quite clear that the main advantage of the reciprocity method of calibration over any other method is that it is not necessary to know the characteristics of any of the transducers used.

By dividing equation 9.9 by 9.10 the value of M_2 can be found. It will be left as an exercise for the reader to show how M_1, M_2, and M_3 can be determined if all three transducers are reversible.

Closed Chamber Reciprocity Calibration

At lower frequencies it is possible to use the reciprocity technique for a closed chamber calibration of a microphone using three transducers T_1 (test microphone), T_2 (reversible microphone) and T_3 (source), as before (see *Figure 44*).

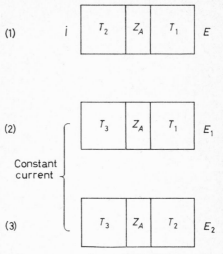

Figure 44. Arrangement of transducers for a closed chamber reciprocity calibration

Because the dimensions of the chamber are small compared with wave-length it is assumed that both acoustic pressure p and volume velocity U_v are constant over the whole chamber; they are related in accordance with the expression

$$p/U_v = Z_A \qquad \dots (9.13)$$

where Z_A is the acoustic impedance of the chamber (see equation 5.1). The chamber may be considered to be an expanding and contracting cavity, the diaphragm of the source acting as a piston, and as such will have an acoustic capacitance C_A given by equation 5.5 as

$$C_A = V/\rho c^2$$

126

where V is the volume of the chamber and c the acoustic velocity. Hence:

$$Z_A = 1/\omega C_A = \rho c^2/\omega V \qquad \dots (9.14)$$

where $\omega = 2\pi f$. From the expressions $M = E/p$ and $S = p/i$ and the reciprocity relationship given by equation 9.4, it is seen that:

$$M = S/Z_A \qquad \dots (9.15)$$

Hence for the transducers T_1 and T_2 we have that:

$$M_1 = E/p = E/iS = (E/iZ_A) . (1/M_2)$$

i.e.,

$$M_1 M_2 = E/iZ_A = (E/i) . (\omega V/\rho c^2) \qquad \dots (9.16)$$

As before if T_1 and T_2 are, in turn, placed in the chamber with T_3 actuated by the same current to produce respective open-circuit voltages E_1 and E_2, we have that:

$$M_1/M_2 = E_1/E_2 \qquad \dots (9.17)$$

Hence

$$M_1 = \{(E/i)(E_1/E_2)/Z_A\}^{\frac{1}{2}} \text{ V per newton m}^{-2} \qquad \dots (9.18)$$

using M-K-S. units.

Frequency Measurements

General Considerations

Acoustic frequencies, both audio and ultrasonic, are usually measured by comparing the source with a standard. One way is to use the method of Lissajous figures (see Chapter 1, page 3), which are obtained on the screen of a cathode ray oscilloscope by connecting the electrical outputs of the test and standard source to the X and Y plates, respectively. Alternatively, one can use the method of beats (see Chapter 1, page 4) where the two frequencies to be compared are sufficiently close together. To determine which of the two frequencies is higher, if a continuously variable frequency standard is not available, one uses two standard sources having frequencies close together and noting whether the number of beats per second increases or decreases when one standard is substituted for the other.

127

FUNDAMENTAL ACOUSTIC MEASUREMENTS

Standard Sources of Frequency

Standards of frequency for acoustics are either mechanical or electrical in operation. The simplest is a solid rod or plate suitably clamped and set up into sustained vibrations of constant amplitude, at a resonant frequency, by an electro-mechanical device. Two commonly used mechanical standards are the electrically maintained tuning fork and the quartz crystal, the latter being more suitable for ultrasonic frequencies and the former for audio frequencies. Both these devices have the advantage of very high Q factors, which result in very narrow frequency bandwidths. The quartz crystal, for example, has a Q factor of approximately 250,000 when properly mounted in vacuo, and provided that the ambient physical conditions are properly controlled, the stability of the frequency can be as high as 1 in 10^8.

The mechanical standards mentioned above will provide fixed frequencies only. If a variable frequency standard is required one must use an electrical oscillator which is calibrated against fixed frequency standards; in many cases the oscillations are controlled by piezoelectric crystals.

Measurements of Propagation Constants

General Considerations

The constants of acoustic propagation usually measured are the velocity and absorption coefficient of plane waves; these determine some of the physical properties of a medium (see Chapter 4). To satisfy the conditions for plane waves it is usual to perform the measurements at high ultrasonic frequencies. A fuller account of these measurements has been provided by the author elsewhere[2], and in this chapter we shall describe the two most important methods of measurement, namely the pulse and the resonance techniques. For propagation in solids it is essential that there is no air gap between the transducer and the specimen, otherwise waves are not propagated into the specimen (see Chapter 3, page 32). A liquid couplant is thus necessary; this can be either a film of liquid, such as oil, or a liquid in which both the transducer and specimen are immersed.

MEASUREMENTS OF PROPAGATION CONSTANTS

The Pulse Technique

The pulse technique consists of passing short trains of sound waves of a given frequency through the medium and noting the time taken for the sound to travel a measured distance. The velocity of sound in the medium is thus determined. The value of the absorption coefficient is obtained by comparing the amplitude of the vibrations of the receiving transducer for different path lengths and using equation 2.22a. For the pulse technique one can use either two separate transducers, one acting as the source and the other as the receiver or, as is more common, a single reversible transducer which acts as both source and receiver, provided that there is some means of reflecting the waves back along the path of incidence. At ultrasonic frequencies piezoelectric transducers are used for measurements in solids and liquids and it is possible to propagate frequencies of up to thousands of megacycles. For gases, however, it is not always easy to match a piezoelectric crystal with the medium owing to the enormous difference between their characteristic impedances (see Chapter 3, page 32); however, successful measurements have been made in gases using electrostatic transducers at frequencies as high as 1 Mc/s.

Because of the very short acoustic path lengths involved, electronic methods are used for the measurement of time; a block diagram of a typical form of apparatus is depicted in *Figure 45*, which shows the arrangement for a solid, using a single reversible transducer. For a fluid the path length can be varied by means of a reflector placed parallel with the source.

The apparatus is operated by means of a trigger which actuates simultaneously the time-base control and the pulse generator. At the same time a signal is passed via the amplifier to the Y plates of the cathode ray oscilloscope; a peak A thus appears at the left-hand side of the screen. Triggering occurs at regular intervals with a frequency which may range from about 50 to 1,000 c/s. Where a frequency of 50 c/s is used it is common practice to use the a.c. mains as a trigger. The transmitting transducer is excited at the required frequency by means of the radio-frequency oscillator, the

129

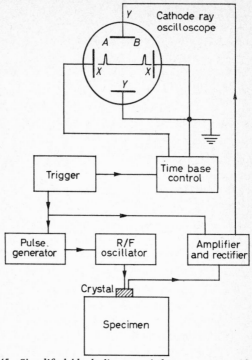

Figure 45. Simplified block diagram of the apparatus used for the pulse technique

output of which is controlled by the pulse generator. In this way, intermittent trains of ultrasonic waves are propagated in the medium. These waves are, in due course, picked up by the receiving crystal and the induced electrical signals are amplified, rectified if necessary, and fed to the Y plates of the oscilloscope to give the peak B. Because of the time delay due to the sound travelling through the solid, the peak B is displayed further along the time-base. Since the time-base frequency is synchronized with the pulse repetition frequency, the peaks A and B remain stationary on the screen. Where the time-base is calibrated, the time taken for the pulse to travel through the specimen is determined by measuring the distance between A and B. The speed of sound is then obtained by dividing the measured value of the acoustic path length by the time obtained in this way. The time-base may be calibrated either by feeding a signal from a standard frequency source to the Y plates of the oscilloscope or by sending pulses through a material in which the velocity of sound is known.

The value of the absorption coefficient is obtained by measuring the relative heights of the peak B for different path lengths. The path length cannot be varied continuously for solids as it can for liquids but if the time-base is contracted sufficiently, a number of equally spaced peaks having heights which decrease exponentially with distance are observed, each peak being separated by the time taken for the waves to travel from the source to the reflecting surface and back. The absorption coefficient can be determined directly from the decrements of the peak heights (see equation 2.22a).

An important application of the pulse method is the detection of flaws such as cracks, inclusions, and blow-holes in metals. Some of the incident sound will be reflected at the defect and return to the transducer earlier than the sound reflected from the lower surface of the specimen; an additional peak will thus appear on the screen of the oscilloscope between A and B. The position of this extra peak will locate the defect, and the height of the peak may indicate the extent of the flaw. The pulse method can also be used as a thickness gauge for solids, provided that the velocity of sound in the specimen is known; this is extremely useful when access is available only to one surface of the sample.

The Resonance Technique

The resonance technique can be used for measuring acoustic velocities in solids, liquids, and gases. This again is best carried out at ultrasonic frequencies. For liquids and gases a quartz crystal transducer, generally operated at its fundamental frequency, is used reversibly as a combined source and receiver; stationary waves are obtained between the source and a movable reflector placed parallel with it.

FUNDAMENTAL ACOUSTIC MEASUREMENTS

Periodic variations of the current through the transducer are obtained as the reflector is moved (see *Figure 46*); sharp minima (for a gas) or sharp maxima (for a liquid) appear for positions of the reflector for resonance. The distance between adjacent resonance positions for the reflector is one

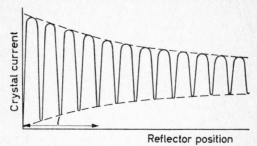

Reflector position

Figure 46. Variation of current in the transducer with the position of the reflector for a gas-filled ultrasonic interferometer

half wave-length and, if the frequency of the source is known, the velocity in the medium can be calculated. The value of the absorption coefficient can be determined from an expression which is a function of the decrement of the peaks (or troughs) of the curve and the peak (or trough) widths.

For solids it is not possible to vary the path length and, instead, the frequency is varied through harmonics. One method, used at ultrasonic frequencies, is to use a crystal source which resonates at a frequency above the highest exciting frequency to be used. The transducer, suitably coupled to the medium by a film of oil, is excited into forced vibrations by continually varying the frequency. When a resonant frequency is reached a suitable indicator will give a maximum response. The difference between two consecutive resonant frequencies is equal to the fundamental frequency of the specimen, for which the thickness is equal to one half wave-length.

To obtain the value of the absorption coefficient of a solid by the resonance method one uses the damping capacity technique. The specimen, usually in the form of a bar, is clamped with the least constraint at a nodal position, preferably in a vacuum, and excited by a transducer attached to one end. One can either excite the transducer at the fundamental frequency of the specimen, switch off the exciting current and then observe the logarithmic decrement δ or excite it over a continuous range of frequencies about the natural frequency of the bar, plot the frequency response curve, and hence obtain the mechanical Q factor Q_m (see Chapter 1, page 13). Because the energy of the oscillations is governed by the size of the solid sample, there is a practical upper limit of about 50 kc/s to the frequencies used for the damping capacity method.

REFERENCES

[1] Beranek, L. L. *Acoustic Measurements*. 1949. New York; Wiley/London; Chapman and Hall
[2] Blitz, J. *Fundamentals of Ultrasonics*. 1963. London; Butterworths

FURTHER READING

Mason, W. P. *Physical Acoustics and the Properties of Solids*. 1958. New York; Van Nostrand

See also the bibliography at the end of Chapter 8

INDEX

Italic figures denote references extending to subsequent pages.

Absorbents, *91*
Absorption, *61, 91*
    fluids, 61
    solids, 63
Absorption coefficient
    absorbents, *91, 95*
    measurements, *128*
    media, 23, 62
Amplitude, 2
Analogies
    electroacoustical, *68*
    electromechanical, *65*
Anechoic chamber, 119
Angular frequency, 2
Antinode, 38
Architectural acoustics, *89*
Attenuation, 23
Audibility, threshold of, 80
Auditoria, *89*

Bar, solid, 53, *57*
Beats, *4*, 127
Bell, 59
Buildings, 89

Capacitance, acoustic, 70
Cavity resonator, *71*, 91
Critical damping, 9

Damped vibrations, *6*
Damping capacity
    technique, *132*
Decibel, 22
Diffraction, *44*
Doppler effect, 27

Ear, response, *80*
Earphones, *107*

Electrostatic actuator, 121
Enclosure
    absorption in, *92*
    decay of
        sound in, *93*
    growth of
        sound in, *93*
Energy density, 21
Equal loudness curves, *81*
Eyring's formula, 95

Feeling, threshold of, 80
Filters, acoustic, *71*
Fourier's theorem, *6*
Fraunhofer zone, 45
Frequency, 2
    fundamental, 5, 40
    measurement of, *127*
    standards, 128
Frequency analysis, *87*
Fresnel zone, 45

Harmonics, 5, 40
Hearing, *80*
Hearing loss, 82
Helmholtz resonator, *71*, 91
Horn, *54, 77*, 110
    conical, *55*
    exponential, *56, 77*
Hot-wire microphone, 122

Impedance
    acoustic, 69, *73, 77*
    characteristic, 20, *30*, 33
    mechanical, 12
    specific acoustic, *20*, 25
Inertance, 69
Intensity, *21*
    diffuse, 93
    measurement, *119*

INDEX

Lissajous figures, *3*, 127
Listening conditions, *89*
Logarithmic decrement, 11, 23
Loudness, *80*
Loudspeaker, *107*
  direct radiation, *108*
  horn, *110*
  voltage response, 110

Masking, 82
Membrane, 61, 91
Microphone, *99*
  carbon, 102
  condenser, *103*
  crystal, *104*
  directional properties, 101
  moving coil, 104
  response, 101
  ribbon, 104
  sensitivity, 101
Microphone calibration, *120*
  closed chamber, *119*
  comparison method, 121
  direct actuation, *120*
  free-field, 119
  reciprocity
    closed chamber, *126*
    free-field, *123*

Node, 38
Noise, *84*
  elimination of, *86*, 89
  investigation of, *87*

Open-window area, 92

Partials, 5, 40
Phase angle, 2
Phon, *81*
Piston, infinite baffle, *44*
Plates, *59*
Propagation constants,
  measurements of, *128*
Pulsatance, 2
Pulse technique, *129*

'*Q*' factor, 13, 23
Quality, 6, 42

Radiation, pressure of, *22*
Radiometer, 122
Rayleigh disc, *121*
Reciprocity, *123*
Recording, *115*
  magnetic methods, 117
  mechanical methods, 116
  optical methods, *116*
  stereophonic, 115
Reflection
  normal incidence, *30*
  oblique incidence, *34*
  total internal, *35*
Reflection coefficient, 32
Refraction, *34*
Reproduction of sound, *115*
Resonance, 12
  half wave-length, *40*, 77
  quarter wave-length, *41*, 76
  stationary waves, *39*, 76
Resonance technique, *131*
Resonator, Helmholtz, *71*
Reverberation chamber, 96
Reverberation time, 90, *94*
Rod, solid, 53, *57*

Sabin, 95
Sabine's formula, 94
Scattering, Rayleigh, 48, 63
Simple harmonic motion, *1*
Siren, *114*
Sone, 83
Sound level meter, 87
Stationary wave ratio, 39
String, stretched, *60*
Suspended particles, *122*

Threshold intensity, 80
Timbre, 6, 42
Time period, 2
Transducer, 99
  ultrasonic, *111*
Transformation factor, 71
Transformer, acoustic, 70

135

Transmission coefficient, 32
Tube, *53*, *73*
Tuning fork, 59

Ultrasonic measurements, *128*
Ultrasonic oscillator
  magnetostrictive, *112*
  mechanical, *114*
  piezoelectric, *111*
Ultrasonic whistle, *114*
Ultrasonics, *111*

Velocity
  gases, *48*
  group, *26*
  liquids, *48*
  longitudinal wave, *18*, 33, *49*
  measurements, *128*
  plane waves, *18*, *49*
  shear wave, *51*
  solids, 51
  transverse wave, *51*, *57*, 60
Vibrations
  control of, 13
  damped, *6*
  elastic, *1*
  flexural, *57*

Vibrations—*cont.*
  forced, *11*
  isolation of, *84*, 89
  simple harmonic, 1

Wave
  equation, 16
  motion, *15*
  number, 17
  propagation, *15*
Wave-length, 17
Waves
  compression, 16
  elastic, 1
  flexural, *57*
  longitudinal, 16
  plane, 16
  shear, 16, 51
  spherical, 16, *23*
  standing (see Waves,
    stationary)
  stationary, *36*, *76*, 97
    resonance, *39*, *76*
    two-dimensional, 43
    three-dimensional, *43*
  surface, 36
  torsion, 57
  transverse, 16